Reteach
Blackline Masters

Level 2

Mc Graw Hill **SRA**

Columbus, OH

SRAonline.com

 SRA

Send all inquiries to this address:
SRA/McGraw-Hill
4400 Easton Commons
Columbus, OH 43219-6188

ISBN: 978-0-07-610396-6
MHID: 0-07-610396-X

3 4 5 6 7 8 9 BCH 13 12 11 10 09 08

Unit 1 Kindness

Unit 2 Let's Explore

Unit 3 — Around the Town

Unit 4 Look Again

⑤ Unit 5 Courage

Unit 6 America's People

Name _____ Date _____

The /ā/ Sound Spelled *a* and *a_e*

Focus

The /ā/ sound sounds like the name of the letter *a*. Two ways that the /ā/ sound can be spelled are:

- *a*   lady
- *a_e*   cake

Practice

shady	chase	lazy	face	table

Write the word from the box that rhymes with each word below.

1. race _____

2. able _____

3. vase _____

4. lady _____

5. hazy _____

Name _____ Date _____

/ī/ spelled *i* and *i_e*

Focus

The /ī/ sound sounds like the name of the letter *i*. Two ways the /ī/ sound can be spelled are:

- *i*   tiny
- *i_e*   rice

Practice

shiny	pricy	time	pride	smile

Change the letter or letters to make a word from the box. The spelling of the /ī/ sound will stay the same.

1. lime   -l   +   t   = _____

2. file   -f   +   sm   = _____

3. slide   -sl   +   pr   = _____

4. tiny   -t   +   sh   = _____

5. icy   +   pr   = _____

Name _____ Date _____

Selection Vocabulary

care	share	feelings	kind	precious

Read each sentence below. Circle the best definition for the boldfaced word.

1. Maria couldn't wait to **share** her birthday cake with her friends. Does **share** mean:
   a. to look after
   b. to divide into portions and give to others as well as to oneself.

2. The new baby was so **precious** to his mother and father. Does **precious** mean:
   a. loved and cherished
   b. an emotion, such as joy, fear, sadness

3. It was so **kind** of you to give me a ride home. Does **kind** mean:
   a. gentle, generous, and friendly
   b. loved and cherished

4. Enrique promised he would **care** for his new puppy. Does **care** mean:
   a. an emotion, such as joy, fear, sadness
   b. to look after

5. Sarah hurt my **feelings** when she wouldn't let me join the team. Does **feelings** mean:
   a. an emotion, such as joy, fear, sadness
   b. gentle, generous, and friendly

Name _____ Date _____

/ā/ spelled *a* and *a_e*
/ī/ spelled *i* and *i_e*

Focus

The /ā/ sound sounds like the name of the letter *a*. Two ways it can be spelled are:

a_e   *cake*

a   *apron*

The /ī/ sound sounds like the name of the letter *i*. Two ways it can be spelled are:

i_e   *fine*

i   *mind*

Practice

| bake | care | mild | time | able | ride |

Rhyming Strategy

Write the spelling word from the box that rhymes with each pair of words below.

1. shake   make   _____   **4.** share   stare   _____

2. lime   chime   _____   **5.** wide   tide   _____

3. table   cable   _____   **6.** child   wild   _____

Name _____ **Date** _____

Common and Proper Nouns

Focus
- A **common noun** names general people, places, and things.

Examples

doctor, street, team

A **proper noun** names specific people, places, and things. Proper nouns are always **capitalized**.

Examples

Dr. Jones, Main Street, New York Yankees

Practice   **Write *common* or *proper* on the line for each noun.**

1. zebra _____

2. Pennsylvania _____

3. Ethan _____

4. chair _____

Underline the proper nouns in the sentences. Circle the common nouns.

1. Matthew's favorite basketball team is the Chicago Bulls.

2. Chicago is a city in Illinois.

3. The state of Illinois was the place where Abraham Lincoln lived.

Name _____ Date _____

The /ō/ Sound Spelled o and o_e

Focus

The /ō/ sound sounds like the name of the letter o. Two ways that the /ō/ sound can be spelled are:

o   go

o_e   vote

Practice

Write the word from the box that rhymes with each word below. The word will have the same spelling for the /ō/ sound.

so	told	role	nose	most

1. hole   _____

2. go   _____

3. gold   _____

4. host   _____

5. close   _____

Name _____ Date _____

The /ū/ Sound Spelled *u* and *u_e*

Focus

The /ū/ sound sounds like the name of the letter *u*. Two ways that the /ū/ sound can be spelled are:

u   menu

u_e   use

Practice   **Write each word from the box in the correct column.**

| menu | cute | human | refuse |
| mule | music | unicorn | huge |

Spelled *u*   **Spelled *u_e***

_____   _____

_____   _____

_____   _____

_____   _____

Name _____ Date _____

Selection Vocabulary

litter	glows	dawn	engines	witness

 **Practice** **Read the clues below. Write the word on the line that solves each riddle.**

1. I am another word for *trash*. Many people pick me up along the roadside to keep it clean. I rhyme with the word *glitter*. _____

2. I am the time each morning when daylight first begins. I am the opposite of *dusk*. I rhyme with the word *lawn*. _____

3. I am a plural noun that ends in s. I help cars, planes, and trucks run. _____

4. I am a word that means "to see or hear something". I start with the letter *w*. _____

5. I am a word that describes what a candle, a lightbulb, and a firefly does. I rhyme with the word *knows*. _____

Name _____ Date _____

/ō/ spelled o and o_e
/ū/ spelled u and u_e

Focus

The /ō/ sound sounds like the name of the letter o. Two ways that the /ō/ sound can be spelled are:

o   only

o_e   note

The /ū/ sound sounds like the name of the letter u. Two ways that the /ū/ sound can be spelled are:

u   unicorn

u_e   use

Practice

cure	nose	most	unit	menu	joke

Visualization Strategy

Circle the correctly spelled word. Then write the word.

1. younit   unit   _____

2. noes   nose   _____

3. cure   cuer   _____

4. jok   joke   _____

5. menue   menu   _____

6. most   moste   _____

Name _____ Date _____

Action Verbs

Focus
- **Action verbs** are words that tell what someone or something is doing. They are the words in a sentence that tell what is happening.

Examples
Abigail **walked** to school.
Erin **rides** her bike.
My sister and I **ran** all the way home.

Practice Circle the action verbs in the following list of words.

bicycle	glows	throw
football	chair	stomp
jumps	computer	talked

Underline the action verb or verbs in each sentence.

1. I helped my dad wash the car on Saturday.

2. He scrubbed it with soap, and I sprayed it with water.

3. I dried it off with a towel.

4. Dad drove the car back into the garage.

5. Then, he gave me a big hug.

Name _____ **Date** _____

/ā/ Spelled *a* and *a_e*
/ī/ Spelled *i* and *i_e*

Focus
- /ā/ spelled *a* = able
- /ā/ spelled *a_e* = bake
- /ī/ spelled *i* = icy
- /ī/ spelled *i_e* = bike

Practice **Read each sentence. Choose the word that best completes each sentence. Write the word on the line.**

1. Write your _____ at the top of the page.

nam   name   naem

2. What _____ of cereal do you like?

kid   kide   kind

3. It is _____ for soccer practice.

time   tide   tid

4. Please put the soup on the _____.

tale   table   taebl

5. We took our boat out on the _____.

lack   lak   lake

6. I had an _____ for the science project.

idea   ieda   ide

7. Place each _____ in the bag.

iteme   iteam   item

8. The _____ gets fussy when he is hungry.

babe   baby   baeb

Name _____ Date _____

/ō/ Spelled *o* and *o_e*
/ū/ Spelled *u* and *u_e*

Focus

- /ō/ spelled *o* = open
- /ō/ spelled *o_e* = stone
- /ū/ spelled *u* = unit
- /ū/ spelled *u_e* = use

Practice Choose a word from the box that best completes the sentence.

stove	usually	museum	hope	only	cute

1. I _____ we can go camping this weekend.

2. Marcy likes going to the _____ to see the dinosaur skeletons.

3. You should never touch a hot _____.

4. The new puppy is very _____.

5. People do not _____ wear shorts in the winter.

6. Lamont has three brothers but _____ one sister.

Name _____ Date _____

Selection Vocabulary

shoemaker	leather	finest	elves	flash

Practice Read each sentence below. Circle the correct definition for the boldfaced word.

1. Santa Claus has many **elves** who help him make toys. Does **elves** mean:
   a. types of fairies   **b.** someone who makes shoes

2. I'll be back in a **flash**. Does **flash** mean:
   a. material made from the skin of an animal   **b.** an instant

3. The **shoemaker** made my mother a pair of loafers. Does **shoemaker** mean:
   a. a type of fairy   **b.** someone who makes shoes

4. **Leather** can be made from cow skin or deer skin. Does **leather** mean:
   a. material made from the skin of an animal   **b.** a type of fairy

5. The peaches were the **finest** I had ever tasted. Does **finest** mean:
   a. an instant   **b.** nicest

Name _____ **Date** _____

Sequence

Focus The more you know about the time that things happen in a story and the order in which things happen, the better you can understand the story.

Here are some words that tell the **time** or when things happen.

today, this morning, once upon a time

Here are some words that tell the **order** in which things happen.

first, then, finally

Practice A **Read the sentences. Underline the time or order word or words in each sentence.**

1. Let's do our homework. Then, we can play soccer.

2. Today I have a dentist appointment.

3. The last thing to do is to lock the door.

4. Yesterday my dog got loose.

5. Once upon a time, a dragon lived in a cave.

6. This morning I had cereal for breakfast.

7. Before you leave, please finish your chores.

Comprehension • *Reteach*

Name _____ **Date** _____

Use the words in the box to complete the sentences.

today	finally	before	earlier	next

1. I got up _____ anyone else in my family.

2. Bonnie wanted to be the _____ one to get her picture taken.

3. We are going to the library _____.

4. Phil said he had seen the lunch box _____ in the day.

Practice B   **Write a sentence using one of the words or phrases in the box below.**

tonight	once	the next morning

_____

_____

_____

Name _____ Date _____

Review: Lessons 1 and 2
/ā/ spelled *a* and *a_e* and /ī/ spelled *i* and *i_e* and /ō/ spelled *o* and *o_e* and /ū/ spelled *u* and *u_e*

Focus The long a, long i, long o, and long u sounds sound like the names of the letters *a, i, o,* and *u.* Two ways that each of these long vowel sounds can be spelled are:

a and *a_e*   *o* and *o_e*

i and *i_e*   *u* and *u_e*

Practice | wild   label   bonus   huge   vine   spoke made   use |

Meaning Strategy
Complete each sentence with a spelling word from the box. Then read the sentence aloud.

1. Grapes grow on a _____.

2. I like it when our teacher puts a _____ question on the test.

3. Read the _____ to see what ingredients are in the soup.

4. May I _____ your pencil?

5. Raccoons are _____ animals.

6. Jessica _____ the soccer team for the first time.

7. Adam _____ in a loud voice so that everyone could hear him.

8. We watched as a _____ boulder rolled down the hillside.

Name _____ Date _____

Linking Verbs and Helping Verbs

Focus

• **Linking Verbs** join or connect parts of sentences to make them complete. Linking verbs *do not* show action.

Examples

Roland **is** a volleyball player. Carlos **was** a baker.

• **Helping verbs** are used with action verbs to help tell when something is happening.

Examples

The girls **were** playing baseball. The boys **are** walking on the field.

Practice **Read the following sentences. Write** *linking* **or** *helping* **on the line to describe the boldfaced verb.**

1. Elizabeth Dole **was** president of the Red Cross. _____

2. Gloria **is** hoping to be president. _____

3. Bill Clinton **was** president. _____

4. Someone **is** always president. _____

5. The President **was** traveling the country. _____

Name _____ **Date** _____

The /ē/ Sound Spelled e and e_e

Focus

The /ē/ sound sounds like the name of the letter e. Two ways that the /ē/ sound can be spelled are:

e	he
e_e	these

Practice

me	zebra	these	Steve	compete	even

Write each word from the box on the line in the correct column.

Spelled e   **Spelled e_e**

_____   _____

_____   _____

_____   _____

_____   _____

Name _____ Date _____

Review: Long Vowels

Focus | **Long vowel sounds** sound like the name of the vowel: *a, e, i, o,* or *u*. Two ways that long vowel sounds can be spelled are:

- Vowel by itself: *a, e, i, o, u*
- Vowel_silent e: *a_e, e_e, i_e, o_e, u_e*

Practice

lake	lion	nose	ride	rake	table
go	menu	race	puny		

Choose the word from the box that best completes each sentence. Write the word on the line.

1. Have you ever taken a _____ on a bus?

2. Please set the _____ for dinner.

3. Michael wanted to _____ to his aunt's house for the weekend.

4. Your _____ is in the middle of your face.

5. Chelsea and Jared took a boat out on the _____.

6. Slow and steady wins the _____.

7. The mouse looked _____, but he was still able to help set the _____ free.

8. In the fall, I have to help _____ leaves in the yard.

9. The cheeseburger is my favorite item on the _____.

Name _____ Date _____

Selection Vocabulary

snoozing	furious	repay	raged	gnaw

 **Practice**   **Read each sentence below. Circle the best definition for the vocabulary word in bold.**

1. I wanted to **repay** Christina for buying me a popsicle. Does **repay** mean:

    a. pay back   **b.** to act violently

2. Our dog likes to **gnaw** on bones. Does **gnaw** mean:

    a. take a quick nap   **b.** to chew

3. Mom was **furious** when we started throwing food at the table. Does **furious** mean:

    a. very angry   **b.** taking a quick nap

4. Dad was **snoozing** on the couch after mowing the lawn. Does **snoozing** mean:

    a. taking a quick nap   **b.** to pay back

5. The bull **raged** when it was closed in its pen. Does **raged** mean:

    a. to chew   **b.** to act violently

Name _____ Date _____

Reality and Fantasy

Focus Fables are stories that teach a moral or lesson to the reader. Fables contain elements of *fantasy,* such as animals that talk, and elements of **reality.** It is important to be able to distinguish between reality and fantasy.

- **Fantasy elements** *could not happen* in the real world. An example would be a talking mouse.

- **Reality elements** *could happen* in the real world. An example would be a mouse that eats crumbs off of the floor.

Practice A Read each idea below. Write on the line whether it is *fantasy* or *reality*.

1. Penguins live near the water. _____

2. A walrus lives in a house and wears a suit. _____

3. A talking tree. _____

4. Birds build nests. _____

5. An ant helping an elephant. _____

6. A snake driving a car. _____

7. Ducks laying eggs. _____

8. Wolves hunt deer. _____

Name _____ **Date** _____

Read the short story below. Write three elements of fantasy and three elements of reality from the story in the correct column.

One sunny day, a beaver got out of his cozy bed and walked out of his front door. He headed over to the river to start building a dam. On the way, he spotted a bear lying in a cave. As he got closer, he heard the bear crying and shouting, "Help!" The bear was trapped under some fallen logs. The beaver used his sharp, strong teeth to chew through the logs. "Thank you!" shouted the bear. "How can I repay your kindness?" "You can give me a ride on your back down to the river." "I would be glad to," said the bear. The two friends went off together.

Fantasy	Reality
_____	_____
_____	_____
_____	_____

Practice B **Write one example of an element of fantasy, and one example of an element of reality.**

Fantasy: _____

Reality: _____

Comprehension • *Reteach*

Name _____ **Date** _____

/ē/ spelled e and e_e

Focus   The /ē/ sound sounds like the name of the letter e. Two ways it can be spelled are:

e	*elect*
e_e	*here*

Practice

these	hero	beside	repay	meter	pretend

Visualization Strategy

Circle the correctly spelled word. Then write the word on the line.

1. beeside   beside   _____

2. hereo   hero   _____

3. meter   meater   _____

4. pretend   preetend   _____

5. reapay   repay   _____

6. these   theeze   _____

Name _____ **Date** _____

Subject and Predicate

 Focus

- Sentences must have a **subject** and a **predicate** to be complete.

- The **subject** tells who or what the sentence is about.

Examples

Jean is my best friend.

My oldest brother is going to college.

- The **predicate** tells what the subject *is* or *does*.

Examples

Jean **is my best friend.**

My oldest brother **is going to college.**

Practice Read each sentence. Draw a line under the subject and circle the predicate.

1. Dinosaurs lived many million years ago.

2. No one knows why the dinosaurs died.

3. Some scientists think a huge meteorite hit Earth.

4. It probably caused a large cloud of dust.

5. The dust blocked the sun's light.

6. Earth became dark and the climate changed.

7. The dinosaurs could not adapt to the changes.

Grammar • *Reteach*

Name _____ Date _____

/n/ Spelled *kn_* and /r/ Spelled *wr_*

Focus
- The /n/ **sound** can be spelled *kn_*, with *k* as a silent letter.

Example
    knock

- The /r/ **sound** can be spelled **wr_**, with *w* as a silent letter.

Example
    wrong

Practice Complete each sentence below with a word from the box.

knee	knock	wrap	wrinkle	knot	wrist	knit	write

1. I still need to _____ Emma's birthday gift.

2. Please _____ on the door before entering.

3. Grandma _____ me a sweater for my birthday.

4. Max forgot to _____ his name on his paper.

5. My older brother hurt his _____ while playing tennis.

6. Sydney couldn't get the _____ out of her shoelace.

7. When grapes _____ in the sun, they become raisins.

8. Brett scraped his _____ when he fell on the sidewalk.

Name _____ Date _____

/f/ Spelled *ph* and /m/ Spelled *_mb*

Focus

- The **/f/ sound** can be spelled *ph*, as in the word *phone*.

- The **/m/ sound** can be spelled *_mb*, as in the word *comb*. The *b* is a silent letter.

Practice **Choose the word from the box that best completes each sentence.**

thumb	phone	lamb	climb	elephant	graph

1. We like seeing the African _____ at the zoo.

2. Be quiet while Mom is talking on the _____.

3. Dad had to _____ up the tree to rescue the cat.

4. Yesterday in math, we made a bar _____ of our favorite snacks.

5. Our baby brother likes to suck his _____.

6. The _____ was covered with soft, white fleece.

Underline the /f/ sound or sounds in each word below.

1. alphabet

2. photograph

3. Phillip

4. trophy

Name _____ Date _____

Selection Vocabulary

Practice **Read the clues below. Choose the word from the box that solves each riddle.**

| escalator | palace | yanked | dashing | fastened |

1. I am a large fancy house where a king or queen would live.

What am I? _____

2. This word means "to pull" on something. It is in the past

tense. _____

3. This is what you do with seat belts and buttons. It is in the

past tense. _____

4. You might be doing this if you are in a hurry to get somewhere
or to get away from something quickly. It rhymes with

"flashing". _____

5. I am a moving stairway. You might see me at a shopping mall
or an airport. Be careful when you step on and off of me! What

am I? _____

Name _____ Date _____

Making Inferences

Focus Sometimes a writer does not tell the reader everything. Readers must use what they already know to understand the story.

Example

Kelley grabbed her bat and glove and hurried to the park.

I know that a bat and glove are used in playing baseball and softball, so Kelley must be going to play ball at the park.

Practice **Read each sentence below. Write clues from the sentence that tell what happened. Then write what the clue tells you.**

1. Juan was so excited he couldn't sleep. He got up before the alarm went off and checked his suitcase again.

Clue: _____

Clue: _____

What the clues tell you: _____

Comprehension • **Reteach**

Name _____ **Date** _____

2. The dog wagged his tail as he looked out the window. He barked and ran to the door.

Clue: _____

Clue: _____

What the clues tell you: _____

_____

3. All of the boxes were in the truck. Sally locked the front door. She got in the truck and sadly looked at the house as they drove away.

Clue: _____

Clue: _____

_____

What the clues tell you: _____

_____

Name _____ **Date** _____

/n/ spelled *kn_*
/r/ spelled *wr_*
/f/ spelled *ph*

Focus

The /n/ sound can be spelled *kn_,* with the silent letter *k,* as in the word *knead.*

The /r/ sound can be spelled *wr_,* with the silent letter *w,* as in the word *wrist.*

The /f/ sound can be spelled *ph,* as in the word *phony.*

**Practice**

| knot | wrap | graph | wrist | knit | write |

Consonant-Substitution Strategy

Replace the underlined letter or letters to create a spelling word from the box.

1. gra<u>ss</u> + ph = _____

2. <u>s</u>kit + kn = _____

3. <u>t</u>ap + wr = _____

4. wri<u>st</u> + te = _____

5. kno<u>ck</u> + t = _____

6. <u>m</u>ist + wr = _____

Name _____ Date _____

Capitalization: Beginnings of Sentences

Focus
- The first word of *every* sentence is **capitalized**.

Examples
The library is closed.
Did you do your homework?
I want to go to the zoo.

Practice **Read the following paragraph. Underline the words that should start with a capital letter.**

the solar system is made up of the sun and eight planets. the sun is a star and is at the center of the solar system. earth is the third planet from the sun. neptune is the planet farthest away from the sun. did you know that Saturn has rings around it? i want to be an astronaut so I can travel through the solar system.

Name _____ Date _____

The /ē/ Sound Spelled *ee* and *ea*

Focus
- Two ways the /ē/ sound can be spelled are:
- *ee*, as in the word *bee*
- *ea*, as in the word *each*

Practice   **Write the word from the box that rhymes with each pair of words. The word will have the same spelling of the /ē/ sound.**

sneak	peach	feet	creek	team	beast	green	flee

1. peek   cheek   _____

2. dream   steam   _____

3. beak   leak   _____

4. greet   meet   _____

5. reach   beach   _____

6. feast   least   _____

7. tree   see   _____

8. seen   teen   _____

Name _____ Date _____

The /ē/ *Sound* Spelled e and e_e

Focus Two ways it can be spelled are:

- e, as in the word *be*
- e_e, as in the word *these*

Practice **Read each sentence below. Circle each word in the sentence with the /ē/ sound. Underline the spelling for the /ē/ sound in each word.**

1. Mr. Jones gave us these two assignments for homework this evening.

2. Steve competed in the one hundred meter dash.

3. Be on time for the recital.

4. I will begin to complete the science project tomorrow.

5. Could you repeat the secret knock for me?

Name _____ Date _____

Selection Vocabulary

| insects | cocoon | enemies | invade | tunnels |

Practice Circle the definition that goes with the boldfaced word.

1. In some cities, cars can drive through **tunnels** under the water. Does **tunnels** mean:
  a. underground passageways   **b.** a six-legged bug

2. A caterpillar builds a **cocoon** around itself before it becomes a butterfly. Does **cocoon** mean:
  a. a person or thing that wants to hurt another   **b.** a case that protects an insect while it changes to an adult

3. Angela's brother decided to **invade** her slumber party. Does **invade** mean:
  a. to enter without an invitation   **b.** an underground passageway

4. Ants are **insects** that eat food at picnics. Does **insect** mean:
  a. a six-legged bug   **b.** a person or thing that wants to hurt another

5. If we are kind to our **enemies,** they may learn to be kind to us. Does **enemies** mean:
  a. a six-legged bug   **b.** a person or thing that wants to hurt another

Selection Vocabulary • *Reteach*

Name _____ **Date** _____

Author's Purpose

> **Focus** **Writers** have different reasons for writing.
>
> Writers write to inform.
>
> • Includes facts and information that can be proven
>
> Writers write to entertain.
>
> • Includes funny words and exciting events
>
> Writers write to persuade.
>
> • Includes opinions and facts to support opinions

Practice A **Tell if the sentences were written to *entertain* or to *inform*.**

1. Ants are part of the animal kingdom. They are a type of insect.

These sentences were written to _____.

2. While Morgan was walking through the forest, she heard someone calling her name. "Morgan!" called the wolf. "Why don't you follow me to that small cottage up on the hill?"

These sentences were written to _____.

Name _____ Date _____

Author's Purpose

Practice B In the box are purposes for writing. Read each story title, and then write the best purpose for each story on the line.

inform	entertain	persuade

1. Facts about Insects _____

2. How to Make a Bed _____

3. Fingers, the Piano-Playing Elephant _____

4. Why Cats Make the Best Pets _____

5. How to Take Photographs _____

Name _____ **Date** _____

/ē/ sound spelled ee, *ea*, e, and e_e

Focus

The /ē/ sound sounds like the name of the letter e. It can be spelled:

ee	tr<u>ee</u>
ea	dr<u>ea</u>m
e	m<u>e</u>
e_e	th<u>e</u>s<u>e</u>

Practice

| sleep | east | we | knee | team |

Rhyming Strategy

Write the spelling word from the box that rhymes with each pair of words below.

1. me   she   _____

2. bee   free   _____

3. sheep   deep   _____

4. beam   dream   _____

5. least   feast   _____

Name _____ Date _____

Complete and Incomplete Sentences

Focus

- A **complete sentence** has a subject, a predicate, and expresses a complete thought.

Example

Jeremy ate dinner at home.

Subject: Jeremy

Predicate: ate dinner at home.

- A **sentence fragment** is an incomplete sentence. It is missing either a subject or a predicate.

**Practice** **Read each sentence below. Write _complete_ or _incomplete_ on the line.**

1. Fell down in the backyard. _____

2. Molly enjoyed eating her birthday cake. _____

3. Do you know who won the football game? _____

4. The car. _____

Make each sentence fragment into a complete sentence.

1. The sun _____.

2. _____ played baseball with me last Sunday.

Grammar • _Reteach_

Name _____ **Date** _____

The /ā/ Sound Spelled *ai_* and *_ay*

Focus

Two ways /ā/ can be spelled are:

- *ai_*, as in the word *rain*
- *_ay*, as in the word *play*

Practice Write the word from the box that rhymes with each pair of words below.

sway	nail	chain	laid

1. rain   pain   _____

2. day   play   _____

3. rail   trail   _____

4. paid   maid   _____

Circle the words with the /ā/ *sound* in each sentence below. Underline the spelling for the /ā/ *sound* in each word.

1. May took the train to play with Gail.

2. I wanted to stay away from the trail while it was raining.

Name _____ Date _____

The /ā/ Sound Spelled *a* and *a_e*

Focus Two ways /ā/ can be spelled are:

- *a*, as in the word *able*
- *a_e*, as in the word *wake*

Practice Read each sentence below. Circle the words that have the /ā/ *sound*. Underline the spelling for the /ā/ *sound* in each word.

1. Last April, we went boating on the lake.

2. Mom always wears an apron when she bakes a cake.

3. Please place the forks on the table for dinner.

4. Trace the shape of each letter in your name.

5. Amy dug a hole so we could plant the acorn.

Name _____ Date _____

Selection Vocabulary

chain	trace	outstretched	print	fossil

Practice **Read each sentence below. Circle the best definition for the boldfaced word.**

1. Mom's arms were **outstretched** to greet me when I got off the school bus. Does **outstretched** mean:
   a. reaching out
   b. a row of connected or related circles

2. Claire found an insect **fossil** in her backyard. Does **fossil** mean:
   a. preserved remains
   b. to follow the path of

3. **Trace** the dotted lines with your finger. Does **trace** mean:
   a. reaching out
   b. to follow the path of

4. Jason made a leaf **print** by placing it under paper and rubbing with a crayon. Does **print** mean:
   a. preserved remains
   b. a mark made by pressing

5. Our class made a paper **chain** to decorate the room. Does **chain** mean:
   a. a row of connected or related circles
   b. a mark made by pressing

Name _____ Date _____

Compare and Contrast

Focus

Writers sometimes compare and contrast in a story to make an idea clearer and to make the story more interesting.

- To **compare** means to tell how two or more things are **alike**. Clue words *like, same, as, both, also,* and *too* are used.

- To **contrast** means to tell how two or more things are **different**. Clue words *different* and *but* are used.

Practice A

Look at the two things listed. Explain how the two are alike and how they are different.

bird's nest   house

How are they alike? _____

_____

How are they different? _____

_____

Name _____ Date _____

Practice B Write the type of your favorite television show and your favorite book. Then tell how they are alike and different.

Television show:

_____

_____

Book:

_____

_____

How are they alike?

_____

_____

How are they different?

_____

_____

Name _____ Date _____

/ā/ spelled *ai_*, *_ay*, *a*, and *a_e*

Focus
The /ā/ sound sounds like the name of the letter *a*. It can be spelled:

*ai_*	p<u>ai</u>n
_ay	st<u>ay</u>
a	<u>a</u>pron
a_e	f<u>a</u>d<u>e</u>

Practice

play	paid	base	April	chain	trace

Consonant-Substitution Strategy
Replace the underlined letter or letters to make a spelling word from the box.

1. <u>ch</u>ase + b = _____

2. <u>r</u>ain + ch = _____

3. <u>f</u>ace + tr = _____

4. <u>d</u>ay + pl = _____

5. Apr<u>on</u> + il = _____

6. <u>br</u>aid + p = _____

Spelling • *Reteach*

Name _____ Date _____

Kinds of Sentence

- **Declarative sentences** make a statement and end in a period (.). *The sky is blue.*

- **Interrogative sentences** ask a question and end in a question mark (?). *Is the sky blue?*

- **Imperative sentences** give a command and end in a period (.). *Set the table.*

- **Exclamatory sentences** show great feeling or emotion and end in an exclamation point (!). *Abby, set the table now!*

Practice **Write what kind of sentence each is on the line.**

1. Oak trees grow from acorns. _____

2. Do oak trees grow from acorns? _____ _____

3. Oak trees can grow eighty feet tall! _____

4. Some types of oak trees are: the pin oak, northern red oak,

and white oak. _____

5. Plant an oak tree in your yard and watch it grow.

_____

Name _____ Date _____

/ē/ spelled ee, ea, e, and e_e

Focus The /ē/ *sound* sounds like the name of the letter e. It can be spelled:

- ee, as in the word *tree*
- ea, as in the word *beach*
- e, as in the word *be*
- e_e, as in the word *eve*

Practice Choose the word from the box that rhymes with each word or pair of words below. Write the word on the line. Then, underline the spelling for the /ē/ sound in each word.

bleach	see	eve	feed	complete	meat

1. Steve _____

2. compete _____

3. beat   treat _____

4. seed   reed _____

5. reach   teach _____

6. knee   bee _____

Phonics • *Reteach*

Name _____ **Date** _____

/ā/ spelled *ai_*, *_ay*, *a*, and *a_e*

Copyright © SRA/McGraw-Hill. Permission is granted to reproduce this page for classroom use.

Focus The /ā/ *sound* sounds like the name of the letter *a*. It can be spelled:

- *ai_*, as in the word *rain*
- *_ay*, as in the word *play*
- *a*, as in the word *acorn*
- *a_e*, as in the word *bake*

Practice **Read each sentence below. Circle the words with the /ā/ *sound*. Underline the spelling of the /ā/ *sound* in each word.**

1. Maybe we can bake bread if it rains.

2. Kate placed her apron on the table.

3. I am afraid that Dad will be late today.

4. Did the bagels go stale?

5. Please put away the rake and then you can play.

Name _____ Date _____

Selection Vocabulary

 **Focus**

Sensing *v.* Feeling.

antennae *n.* Plural of **antenna:** An insect feeler.

fussy *adj.* Hard to please.

dull *adj.* Not bright or clear.

cycle *n.* A repeated sequence of events.

Practice **Circle the word in parentheses that makes the most sense in the sentence.**

1. The baby gets awfully (antennae, fussy) when he is hungry or tired.

2. Ken was (sensing, cycle) that John was angry with him.

3. The windows were starting to look (dull, fussy) because they needed to be cleaned.

4. The grasshopper used its (cycle, antennae) to touch and smell the leaf.

5. The life (dull, cycle) of a butterfly is egg, larva, pupa, adult.

Name _____ Date _____

Review: The /ā/ and /ē/ sounds

| reach | acorn | player | sweet | even | tail |

Rhyming Strategy

Say each letter name below. Write the words from the box that have the same sound as the letter name. Then think of and write one more word for each sound.

1. *a*   _____

_____

_____

_____

2. *e*   _____

_____

_____

_____

Name _____ Date _____

Capitalization: Proper Nouns, Titles, and Initials

Focus
- A **proper noun** is a special type of noun. Proper nouns begin with a *capital letter*. A proper noun names a *particular* person, place, or thing.

Examples **M**aureen; **H**ouston, **T**exas; **S**uper **B**owl
- A **title**, which comes before a person's name, is always capitalized.

Examples **D**r. Griffiths; **M**rs. Betz
- **Initials** of a person's name are also capitalized.

Examples **T.J.** Smith

Practice **Underline the proper nouns in the sentences.**

1. Jodi and Scott visited the Detroit Zoo in Michigan.

2. Our class took a trip to the White House.

3. On Saturdays Rose goes to the park.

Rewrite the following names using the correct capitalization.

1. a.j. simon _____

2. president lincoln _____

Name _____ **Date** _____

/ē/ spelled ee, ea, e, and e_e

Focus The /ē/ *sound* sounds like the name of the letter e. It can be spelled:

- ee, as in the word ch<u>ee</u>k
- *ea*, as in the word pl<u>ea</u>se
- *e*, as in the word sh<u>e</u>
- *e_e*, as in the word comp<u>ete</u>

Practice **Write the word from the box that best completes each sentence on the line. Then, underline the spelling for the /ē/ sound in each word.**

reach	maybe	weeks	delete

1. My birthday is less than three _____ away.

2. If you make a mistake while typing, you can press the

_____ key.

3. Mom said that _____ we can watch a movie after dinner.

4. I have to use a stool to _____ the top shelf.

Phonics • *Reteach*

Name _____ Date _____

The /ē/ Sound Spelled _ie_, _y, and _ey

Focus The /ē/ *sound* sounds like the name of the letter *e*. It can be spelled:

- _ie_   bel<u>ie</u>ve
- _y   bab<u>y</u>
- _ey   monk<u>ey</u>

Practice Write the word from the box that best completes each sentence on the line. Then, underline the spelling for the /ē/ *sound* in each word.

thief	messy	turkey	field	puppy

1. Abby had to clean up her _____ room.

2. Our new _____ has brown fur with white spots.

3. The farmer plowed his _____ before he planted corn.

4. Did the police catch the _____ who robbed the store?

5. Every year on Thanksgiving, we have _____ and mashed potatoes.

Name _____ Date _____

Selection Vocabulary

Focus rent   vacant   tenants   examined   deserted

Practice   **Read each sentence below. Circle the best definition for the boldfaced word.**

1. Dr. Turner **examined** Caitlin's eyes. Does **examined** mean:
   a. looked at closely   **b.** left behind

2. The **tenants** of the apartment building had to pay their **rent** at the beginning of each month. Does **tenants** mean:
   a. to look at closely   **b.** people who live in another person's property

   Does **rent** mean:
   a. a regular payment for the right to use property   **b.** empty

3. The parking lot was **vacant** after the store closed. Does **vacant** mean:
   a. one who lives in another's property   **b.** empty

4. Damon **deserted** the burning car and ran to safety. Does **deserted** mean:
   a. empty   **b.** left behind

Name _____ Date _____

Point of View

Focus **Point of view** is how the author decides to tell the story—through a character or through someone outside of the story.

When a story is told from the **first-person point of view.**

• the storyteller is a character in the story.

• the clue words *I, me, my, us,* and *we* are used.

When a story is told from the **third-person point of view.**

• the storyteller is not a character in the story.

• the clue words *she, he, him, they,* and *them* are used.

Practice A **Fill in the circle to tell if the sentence is written from the first-person point of view or the third-person point of view. Underline the word or words in each sentence that help you know the point of view.**

1. Early one morning, a giant bug crawled up my wall.
   first-person point of view   ○ third-person point of view

2. She looked at her long hair in the mirror.
   ○ first-person point of view   third-person point of view

3. Tim and I held a jumping contest.
   first-person point of view   ○ third-person point of view

Comprehension • *Reteach*

Name _____ Date _____

Practice B **Read the paragraph below. Circle each word that gives a clue about who is telling the story. Write the point of view on the line.**

I was standing at the bus stop with my mother. She was holding my hand. We were looking down the street to see if the bus was coming. I could not see it yet. My mother knew I was feeling nervous. She kissed me. It was my first day at the new school.

Point of view: _____

Name _____ Date _____

/s/ sound spelled *ce* and *ci_*
/j/ sound spelled *ge* and *gi_*

Focus

The /s/ sound can be spelled:

ce	r<u>ice</u>
*ci_*	<u>ci</u>rcle

The /j/ sound can be spelled:

ge	ca<u>ge</u>
*gi_*	<u>gi</u>ant

Practice

peace	digit	gem	pencil	circus	large

Visualization Strategy
Circle the word that is spelled correctly. Then write the word.

1. jem   gem   _____

2. circus   cercus   _____

3. dijet   digit   _____

4. peise   peace   _____

5. pencil   pencel   _____

6. large   larj   _____

Spelling • *Reteach*

Name _____ Date _____

Adjectives

Focus

- An **adjective** describes or tells more about a noun or pronoun. Adjectives tell *how many, how much, what color,* or *what kind.*

Example
  He liked a **red** coat.

- There are three **articles:** *a, an,* and *the*. Articles are used before nouns.

Examples
  A banana
  The basket

Practice Underline each adjective.

1. Deer have white tails.

2. There are three eagles in the tree.

3. The wrinkly elephants walked in the jungle.

Circle the articles in the sentences below.

1. A black bear stole our food.

2. The monkey ate the banana.

3. The bluebird sat on a fence.

Reteach • Grammar

Name _____ Date _____

The /s/ sound

Focus The **/s/ sound** can be spelled several different ways:

- ce space
- ci_ circle
- cy icy

Practice **Read each sentence below. Circle the words with the /s/ sound. Underline the spelling for the /s/ sound in each word.**

1. Lucy and Marcy had races at recess.

2. Please sit in the center of the circle.

3. After eating the spicy rice, we got a drink of apple cider.

4. Place the fancy lace napkins beside each plate.

5. The lion ate a juicy piece of steak.

Phonics • *Reteach*

Name _____ Date _____

The /j/ Sound

Focus The /j/ **sound** can be spelled with the letters *ge* and *gi_*.
- *ge*   ca<u>ge</u>
- *gi*   <u>gi</u>ant

Practice

page	gem	large

Write the word from the box that rhymes with each pair of words below.

1. hem   them   _____

2. cage   stage   _____

3. barge   charge   _____

Circle the word in parentheses that best completes each sentence.

1. The (giant, geant) lived at the top of the beanstalk.

2. (Jeraffes, Giraffes) have long necks.

3. The car's (engine, injine) wouldn't start.

Name _____ Date _____

Selection Vocabulary

 **Focus** | trunks | limbs | stems | sprouts | minerals

Practice Choose the vocabulary word from the box that solves each riddle below. Write the word on the line.

1. This word means "the main part of a plant". It connects the

   leaves to the roots. _____

2. This word means "the main part of a tree". Branches grow out

   of it. It rhymes with "chunks". _____

3. These are the parts of the tree that you would grab onto if you
   were climbing it. They are also known as branches. This word

   has a silent *b* in it. _____

4. This describes what a plant does when it is just beginning to

   grow. It rhymes with "shouts". _____

5. These are found underground. They are used as food for
   plants that are growing in the soil. It is the only word in the

   box that has eight letters. _____

Selection Vocabulary • *Reteach*

Name _____ Date _____

Classifying and Categorizing

Focus Readers **classify and categorize** to help keep track of information that they read.

- Name the categories, or the **kinds** of things, characters, or events.

- List the things, characters, or events that fit under each category.

- Sometimes things, characters, or events can fit into more than one category.

Practice A Circle the thing that does not fit in each category.

1. **Things to eat with**
   Fork   plate   slippers   knife

2. **Things to read**
   Books   magazines   map   pillow

3. **Things to listen to**
   Radio   telephone   pie   television

4. **Things to cut with**
   Comb   lawnmower   knife   scissors

Name _____ Date _____

Practice B   Look at the items in the box. Think of two categories to classify the items into. Write the categories. Then, put the items into the correct category.

lemonade	strawberries	coffee	milk
bananas	orange juice	grapes	watermelon

Category: _____   Category: _____

_____   _____

_____   _____

_____   _____

_____   _____

Comprehension • *Reteach*

Name _____ Date _____

/ē/ sound spelled _ie_ and _y
Review: Lesson 4

Focus The /ē/ sound sounds like the name of the letter e. It can be spelled:

_ie_   br**ie**f

_y   ver**y**

The /s/ sound can be spelled:

ce   fa**ce**

ci_   **ci**nder

The /j/ sound can be spelled:

ge   hed**ge**

gi_   **gi**ant

Practice

| funny | chief | cell | field | rigid |

Rhyming Strategy
Write the spelling word from the box that rhymes with each word below.

1. bell   _____   **4.** bunny   _____

2. thief   _____   **5.** yield   _____

3. frigid   _____

Reteach • Spelling

Name _____ **Date** _____

Nouns: Singular and Plural

Focus
- Most nouns can be made **plural** by adding -s to the end of the word.
- Nouns that end in *s, x, z, ss, ch,* or *sh* are made plural by adding -es.
- Nouns that end with a *consonant* and a *y* are made plural by changing the *y* to an *i* and adding -es.
- When a noun ends with a *vowel* and a *y*, an *s* is added.

 **Practice** **Look at the singular and plural nouns below. Underline the correct spelling for each plural noun.**

Singular	Plural	
1. family	familys	families
2. play	plays	plaies
3. box	boxs	boxes
4. dress	dresss	dresses
5. table	tables	tablies
6. lunch	lunchs	lunches

Grammar • *Reteach*

Name _____ **Date** _____

/ī/ spelled _igh, i, and i_e

Focus The /ī/ sounds like the name of the letter *i*. It can be spelled:

- *_igh*   h<u>igh</u>
- *i*   f<u>i</u>nd
- *i_e*   b<u>i</u>k<u>e</u>

kind	write	night	smile	high

Write the word from the box that rhymes with each word below. The word will have the same spelling of the /ī/ sound.

1. pile   _____

2. find   _____

3. kite   _____

4. sigh   _____

5. right   _____

Name _____ Date _____

/ī/ Spelled _y and _ie

Focus The /ī/ sound sounds like the name of the letter *i*. Two ways the /ī/ sound can be spelled are:

- _y   *my*
- _ie   *tie*

Practice **Read each sentence below. Circle the words with the /ī/ sound. Then, underline the spelling for the /ī/ sound in each word.**

1. My brother tried all day to tie his shoes.

2. I like to lie on the grass and watch birds fly up in the sky.

3. Fried chicken and apple pie are my favorite foods.

4. T. J. asked, "Why do I have to wear a tie?"

5. Abby cried when she was hit in the head by the baseball.

Phonics • *Reteach*

Name _____ **Date** _____

Selection Vocabulary

**Focus** practice public recognize automatically
perched

Practice **Read each sentence below. Circle the best definition for the boldfaced word.**

1. Do you **recognize** our camp counselor from last summer? Does **recognize** mean:
   a. do something over and over again
   b. know and remember from before

2. Each night, I must **practice** the piano so that I get better at playing. Does **practice** mean:
   a. do something over and over again to gain skill
   b. sit or rest on a raised place

3. The clock **automatically** chimes each hour. Does **automatically** mean:
   a. sit or rest on a raised place
   b. working by itself

4. The new community center is open to the **public**. Does **public** mean:
   a. to stand, sit or rest on a raised place
   b. for all the people

Name _____ Date _____

Spelling: /ī/ spelled _igh, _y, _ie, i, and i_e

Focus

The /ī/ sound sounds like the name of the letter *i*. It can be spelled:

_igh	h<u>igh</u>
_y	pr<u>y</u>
_ie	t<u>ie</u>
i	<u>i</u>dle
i_e	r<u>i</u>c<u>e</u>

Practice

shy	pie	night	child	mice

Visualization Strategy

Read each pair of words below. Circle the correctly spelled word. Then, write the word on the line.

1. pigh   pie   _____

2. child   chyld   _____

3. night   nyt   _____

4. mighs   mice   _____

5. shy   shie   _____

Name _____ Date _____

Comparative Adjectives and Articles

Focus Some adjectives are called **comparative** because they are used to compare two nouns.

- **Superlative adjectives** compare three or more nouns and mean the most of something. They are formed when the letters –*est* are added to an adjective.

- The articles **a, an,** and **the** are special adjectives called **articles**. *A* is used before a noun that begins with a consonant sound: *a* cookie. *An* is used before a noun that begins with a vowel sound: *An* apple.

Practice Write *comparative* or *superlative* on the line.

1. The Pacific Ocean is **larger** than the Atlantic Ocean.

_____

2. The Pacific Ocean is the **largest** ocean in the world.

_____

For each noun below, circle the correct article that comes before it.

1. A/An tiger   **2.** A/An egg

Name _____ **Date** _____

The /ō/ Sound

Focus The /ō/ *sound* sounds like the name of the letter *o*. It can be spelled:

- _ow   sh<u>ow</u>
- oa_   <u>oa</u>tmeal

Practice

foam	**boat**	**loan**	**snow**
lower	**road**	**borrow**	**toast**

Write the word from the box that rhymes with each word below.

1. groan   _____

2. mower   _____

3. roast   _____

4. coat   _____

5. roam   _____

6. glow   _____

7. load   _____

8. sorrow   _____

Name _____ **Date** _____

The /ō/ Sound

Focus The /ō/ *sound* sounds like the name of the letter *o*. It can be spelled:

- o   g<u>o</u>
- o_e   n<u>ote</u>

Practice

no	old	hose	stone	hope

Choose the word from the box that rhymes with each word below. Write the word on the line.

1. rose   _____

2. bone   _____

3. go   _____

4. fold   _____

5. rope   _____

Name _____ Date _____

Selection Vocabulary

Focus

employees *n.* Plural of employee: a person who works for a person or business for pay.

deposits *n.* Plural of deposit: money added to a bank account.

withdrawals *n.* Plurals of withdrawal: money taken out of a bank account.

borrow *v.* To receive something with the understanding that it must be given back.

vault *v.* A room or compartment that is used to store money or other things of value.

Practice **Read each sentence below. Circle the word in parentheses that best completes the sentence.**

1. Each night, the (employees, vault) of the grocery store put new items on the shelves.

2. We like to (deposit, borrow) library books each weekend.

3. The money at the bank is kept in a large room called a (borrow, vault).

Draw a line to connect each word with its correct definition.

1. deposits   money added to a bank account

2. withdrawals   money taken out of a bank account

Selection Vocabulary • *Reteach*

Name _____ Date _____

Spelling: /ō/ spelled _ow, oa_, o, and o_e

Focus

The /ō/ sound sounds like the name of the letter o. It can be spelled:

_ow	sl<u>ow</u>
oa_	g<u>oa</u>l
o	g<u>o</u>
o_e	h<u>o</u>p<u>e</u>

Practice

store	boat	blow	loan	toad

Consonant-Substitution Strategy

Replace the underlined letter or letters to make a spelling word from the box. The spelling word will have the same spelling for the /ō/ sound.

1. <u>s</u>low + b = _____

2. <u>g</u>oat + b = _____

3. <u>r</u>oad + t = _____

4. <u>sh</u>ore + st = _____

5. <u>gr</u>oan + l = _____

Name _____ Date _____

Capitalization: Days, Months, Cities, and States

> • The names of **days** and **months** are capitalized.
> Examples
>
>   Thursday, April
>
> • The names of **cities** and **states** are capitalized.
> Examples
>
>   Los Angeles, Nebraska

Practice   Rewrite the following words or greetings on the line with the proper capitalization.

1. friday _____

2. new york city _____

3. ohio _____

4. october _____

5. miami _____

6. june _____

7. monday _____

8. texas _____

Grammar • *Reteach*

Name _____ Date _____

/ī/ spelled _igh, i, i_e, _y, and _ie

Focus The /ī/ sound sounds like the name of the letter *i*. It can be spelled:

- *igh*   h<u>igh</u>
- *i*   <u>i</u>dea
- *i_e*   <u>i</u>c<u>e</u>
- *_y*   fl<u>y</u>
- *_ie*   t<u>ie</u>

Practice **Read each sentence below. Circle the word with the correct spelling of the /ī/ sound that best completes the sentence.**

1. Which plate is (myne, mine)?

2. A. J. had a good (iedea, idea) for the science fair.

3. I love pumpkin (pie, py) with whipped cream.

4. After the (lights, lytes) went out, the movie started.

5. Babies (crigh, cry) when they are hungry.

Name _____ Date _____

/ō/ spelled _ow, oa_, o, o_e

Focus The /ō/ *sound* sounds like the name of the letter o. It can be spelled:

- _ow   cr<u>ow</u>
- oa_   b<u>oa</u>t
- o   g<u>o</u>
- o_e   n<u>ose</u>

Practice **Read each sentence below. Circle the word with the correct spelling of the /ō/ *sound*.**

1. Could you (hold, hoaled) the door open for me?

2. Dad and I like to (thro, throw) the ball around in the backyard.

3. Let's go (home, hoame) for lunch.

4. Jessie had eggs, pancakes, and (oatmeal, owtmeal) for breakfast.

5. Would you rather fly or take a (bote, boat)?

Name _____ **Date** _____

Selection Vocabulary

Focus ingredients dough international culture jalapeño

Practice **Circle the correct word that completes each sentence.**

1. To make bagels, you first have to knead the _____.
   a. dough   **b.** international

2. _____ peppers are good on pizza.
   a. culture   **b.** jalapeño

3. We wore costumes to the _____ fair.
   a. international   **b.** ingredients

4. What _____ do you like on your bagels?
   a. dough   **b.** ingredients

5. We are reading about Mexican _____.
   a. culture   **b.** jalapeño

Name _____ Date _____

Fact and Opinion

> **Focus** Writers use facts and opinions to support ideas in their writing.
>
> • A **fact** is a statement that can be proven true.
>
> • An **opinion** is what someone feels or believes is true. An opinion cannot be proven true or false

Ask yourself the question "Can this sentence be proven true?" If it can be proven true, then it is a fact. Write an X next to each sentence that is a fact.

1. _____ Five times five is twenty-five.

2. _____ Basketball is more fun than soccer.

3. _____ My brother should buy a red car.

4. _____ A giraffe is a mammal.

Ask yourself the question "Can this sentence be proven true or false?" If it cannot be proven true or false, then it is an opinion. Write an O next to each sentence that is an opinion.

1. _____ A football field is 100 yards long.

2. _____ Shirts with collars are better than shirts without collars.

3. _____ Rome is in Italy.

4. _____ Only yellow flowers should be planted in gardens.

Comprehension Skill • **Reteach**

Name _____ **Date** _____

Practice B What's your opinion about dinosaurs? Write a sentence stating your opinion.

_____

_____

_____

Write a sentence giving one fact that you know about dinosaurs.

_____

_____

_____

Name _____ Date _____

Spelling: Review Lessons 1 and 2

Focus The long i sound can be spelled *igh, y, ie, i,* and *i_e.*

The long o sound can be spelled *ow, oa, o,* and *o_e.*

 **Practice**

| why | tow | bike | soap | tie | cone |

Meaning Strategy
Fill in the blank with the spelling word from the box that best completes the sentence.

1. I like to ride my _____ to the library after school.

2. _____ did you have to leave so early?

3. Wash your hands with _____ and water before dinner.

4. Would you like your ice cream in a _____ or a dish?

5. The _____ truck pulled our car to the gas station.

6. I am teaching my younger brother how to _____ his shoes.

Spelling • *Reteach*

Name _____ Date _____

Commas: Items in a Series

> • A **comma** is used after each item in a list. The comma helps separate the items when we read. This makes reading a list easier.
>
> Examples
>
> > Jenny had to remember to take her homework, backpack, lunch, and coat to school.

 **Read the following sentences. Add commas where they are needed.**

1. Simone put on her gloves hat scarf and boots before playing in the snow.

2. Apurva's favorite foods are pizza spaghetti and pancakes.

3. Last summer, our family went hiking boating and swimming.

4. Henry had a fever chills and a sore throat.

5. The three primary colors are red yellow and blue.

Name _____ Date _____

The /ū/ Sound

Focus The /ū/ sound sounds like the name of the letter u. It can be spelled:

- _ew   f<u>ew</u>
- _ue   c<u>ue</u>

Practice **Read each sentence below. Circle the words with the /ū/ sound. Then, underline the spelling for the /ū/ sound in each word.**

1. There are a few items that need to be reviewed.

2. The dog was rescued from the burning house.

3. My nephew likes to sit in the first pew at church.

4. Matthew and Abby always argue about which T.V show they will view.

5. Please continue to work for a few minutes.

Name _____ **Date** _____

/ū/ Spelled *u* and *u_e*

Focus The */ū/ sound* sounds like the name of the letter *u*. It can be spelled:

- *u*   <u>u</u>sual
- *u_e*   <u>u</u>s<u>e</u>

Practice

unit	cube	amuse	menu
humor	cute	museum	huge

Write each word from the box in the correct column below.

Spelled *u*	Spelled *u_e*
_____	_____
_____	_____
_____	_____
_____	_____

Day 3

Name _____ Date _____

Selection Vocabulary

Focus taxes cashier routes council elect mayor

Practice Circle the best definition for the boldfaced word.

1. I know two different **routes** to school. Does **routes** mean:
   a. a road, or other course used for traveling
   b. money that people or businesses must pay the government

2. The **cashier** at the grocery store took our money for the food we bought. Does **cashier** mean:
   a. the person who is the head of a city government
   b. a person in charge of paying or receiving money

3. In November, we will **elect** a new governor. Does **elect** mean:
   a. to choose by voting
   b. a road or other course used for traveling

4. The **mayor** of our town made wearing bike helmets a law. Does **mayor** mean:
   a. a person in charge of giving or receiving money
   b. the person who is the head of a city or town government

Selection Vocabulary • *Reteach*

Name _____ **Date** _____

Drawing Conclusions

Focus
- To **draw a conclusion,** a reader should use information that a writer gives about a thing, character, or event. Conclusions must be supported by the information in the story.

Practice A Read each paragraph. Then, draw a conclusion by answering the question.

We made sandwiches and put ice in the cooler. Mother packed lemonade, homemade cookies, cups, and napkins. Our beach towels and chairs were in the car. The sand toys were packed, too. Each of us had on our bathing suit.

Where do you think the people are going?

_____

The day we arrived was perfect. We saw the ocean and walked on the beach. The sunset was beautiful. The next day we visited the local zoo. It will be hard to go home again on Saturday.

Where are these people?

_____

Name _____ **Date** _____

Use what the sentences tell you to answer the question.

- The two slides were shining in the sun.
- The swings were empty.
- The merry-go-round had a father and son on it.
- The see-saw was still.

1. Where does this take place?

_____

- Begin floating by pushing away from the wall.
- Kick your feet.
- Cup your hands as you paddle with your arms.
- Put your face in the water part of the time.

2. What are you doing?

_____

Name _____ Date _____

Spelling: The /ū/ sound spelled
ew, *ue*, *u*, and *u_e*

Focus The /ū/ sound sounds like the name of the
letter *u*. It can be spelled:

ew	v<u>iew</u>
ue	c<u>ue</u>
u	<u>u</u>nit
u_e	c<u>u</u>re

Practice

music	cute	rescue	few	value	mew

Visualization Strategy
**Read each pair of words below. Choose the correctly
spelled word. Then write the word on the line.**

1. fyoo   few   _____

2. music   muesic   _____

3. cute   cewt   _____

4. vallew   value   _____

5. mew   mue   _____

6. reskyoo   rescue   _____

Reteach • Spelling

Name _____ **Date** _____

Subject/Verb Agreement

The subject and verb of a sentence must agree.

Rule

- A **singular subject** must have a **singular verb.**

Rule

- A **plural subject** must have a **plural verb.**

Practice **Underline the correct verb to complete each sentence.**

1. Tadpoles (grow, grows) into frogs.

2. The bat (hang, hangs) upside-down.

Underline the subject. Circle the verb. Write _singular_ or _plural_ on the line.

3. The birds build a nest. _____

4. The bluebird flies south for the winter. _____

Name _____ Date _____

Open and Closed Syllables

Focus

Recognizing syllable patterns will help you know where to divide a multisyllabic word and how to pronounce it.

• An **open syllable** occurs when a syllable ends in a **vowel**.

Examples

ta•ble   no•tice   di•ner

• A **closed syllable** occurs when a vowel is followed by a consonant.

Examples

big•ger   rub•bing   din•ner

Practice

Underline the words with *open syllables*.
Circle the words with *closed syllables*.

| Corner | grocery | secret | writer | fallen |
| Summer | broken | carpet | pencil | between |

Day 1

Name _____ Date _____

The /ū/ Sound

Focus The /ū/ *sound* sounds like the name of the letter *u*. It can be spelled:

- *_ew*   f<u>ew</u>
- *_ue*   c<u>ue</u>
- *u*   <u>u</u>sual
- *u_e*   c<u>u</u>t<u>e</u>

Practice **Underline the spelling for the /ū/ sound in each word below. The first one has been done for you.**

1. neph<u>ew</u>

2. unit

3. mute

4. humid

5. pew

6. view

7. uniform

8. hue

Name _____ **Date** _____

Selection Vocabulary

Focus
aisles   construction   huddled   sharp
arrangement   tingle

Practice   Circle the best definition for the boldfaced word.

1. The penguins **huddled** together to stay warm. Does **huddled** mean:

   a. crowded together

   b. the act of building something

2. We had an **arrangement** to meet at the soccer field. Does **arrangement** mean:

   a. a plan

   b. the space between two rows or sections of something

3. The new skyscraper has been under **construction** all summer. Does **construction** mean:

   a. to crowd together

   b. the act of building something

4. I had to walk down many **aisles** before I found the cereal. Does **aisles** mean:

   a. a plan

   b. the spaces between two rows or sections of something

Name _____ **Date** _____

Spelling: Open and Closed Syllables; Review long u

Focus

An *open syllable* ends in a vowel sound. The vowel sound is usually long.

Example   *ocean*

A closed *syllable* ends in a consonant. The vowel sound before the consonant is usually short.

Example   *apple*

The long u sound sounds like the name of the letter *u*. It can be spelled *ew, ue, u,* and *u_e*.

Practice

Meaning Strategy
Choose the spelling word in the parentheses that best completes the sentence.

1. What time do swimming lessons (begin, cancel)?

2. July is a very hot and (fuel, humid) month.

3. Our coach had to (cancel, wagon) practice because so many people were on vacation.

4. Do you know the answer to five (number, minus) three?

5. I can't wait to (open, until) my birthday gifts!

6. Grandpa pulled us around the zoo in a (person, wagon)

Spelling • *Reteach*

Name _____ Date _____

Plurals, Antonyms, and Synonyms

Focus
- A **plural noun** adds an -s to the end to name more than one person, place, or thing.
- **Antonyms** are words that mean the opposite of another word.
- **Synonyms** are words that mean the same or almost the same as another word.

Practice Add an -s to the end of the word to make it plural.

1. animal _____ **2.** table _____

Circle the antonym of the word in *italics*.

1. My shoes are *wet*.   **2.** The answer is *yes*.
    dry   dirty   four   no

Read each sentence. Write the synonym from the word box to replace the underlined word.

nice	tall	thin	glad	bright

1. My dad's car is very <u>shiny</u>. _____

2. The nurse was very <u>kind</u>. _____

3. I was <u>happy</u> when it was time for recess. _____

Day 3

Name _____ Date _____

Selection Vocabulary

 **Focus**

camouflage	patterns	blend
surroundings	pretenders	mimicry

Practice Read each sentence. Circle the vocabulary word in the parentheses that best fits each sentence.

1. Many animals use (camouflage, pretenders) to protect themselves from enemies.

2. We like to look at our (mimicry, surroundings) when we take a walk.

3. To make a milkshake, you have to (blend, camouflage) milk and ice cream.

4. The (pretenders, patterns) on her shirt were blue and red stripes.

5. Many children are (surroundings, pretenders) on Halloween.

6. Babies use (mimicry, camouflage) to learn how to clap.

Name _____ Date _____

Main Idea and Details

Focus

- A **main-idea sentence** gives the main idea of a paragraph. The other sentences in the paragraph give details about the main idea.

- Often, the main-idea sentence comes first in a paragraph. Having the main idea sentence first helps readers know what the paragraph will be about.

Practice

Read the paragraphs below. Underline the main-idea sentence in each one.

1. Debra's favorite season is winter. She loves to play in the snow and ice skate. In the mornings, she likes the way the frozen ground crunches under her feet. Sometimes her mother makes her hot chocolate for a treat.

2. Saturday is a busy day in my town. Many people start their day at the farmer's market or the bakery. Then, lots of people go to the movies or play at the park.

3. Farming is hard work. The animals need to be fed and let out of the barn. There is always planting or harvesting to be done. Farmers must milk the cows and do other chores, too.

Name _____ **Date** _____

Main Idea and Details

**Read each paragraph. The main idea is missing.
Draw a line under the best main-idea sentence
from the box.**

Shalene stirs the vegetable soup. It is Grandma's favorite. Shalene adds some pepper to the soup. Then, she sets the table for three—her dad, herself, and Grandma.

Shalene is a good cook.

Dinner with Shalene is always fun.

Grandma is coming for dinner.

Moira found some long dresses at a thrift shop. She added feathers, buttons, and shiny ribbons to the long dresses. They were perfect for the scene in the grand ballroom!

Moira is in the class play.

Moira is in charge of the costumes for our class play.

Moira plays the violin.

Name _____ Date _____

Spelling: /o͞o/ spelled *oo*

Focus The /o͞o/ sound sounds like the word *moo*. One way it can be spelled is *oo*.

Practice

| mood | room | pool | soon | bloom | tooth |

Rhyming Strategy

Write the spelling word or words from the box that rhyme with each word below.

1. cool _____

2. moon _____

3. booth _____

4. food _____

5. boom _____ _____

Name _____ Date _____

Subject and Object Pronouns

Focus

- A **pronoun** is a word that takes the place of a noun.

- **Subject pronouns** replace the subjects in sentences.
  Example   **Steven** threw the ball to me.
             He threw the ball to me.

  Subject pronouns: *I, you, he, she, it, we,* and *they.*

- **Object pronouns** replace the objects in sentences.
  Example   Steven threw the ball to **Katie**.
             He threw the ball to **her**.

  Object pronouns: *me, you, him, her, it, us,* and *them.*

Practice   **Underline the subject pronoun in each sentence.**

1. I am learning to play the violin.

2. He played the piano.

3. She enjoys music.

Underline the object pronoun in each sentence.

4. My father gave me Beethoven's music on CD.

5. My mother plays the piano for us.

      Grammar • *Reteach*

Name _____ Date _____

Selection Vocabulary

Focus
hare *n.* A kind of rabbit
scent *n.* A smell.
meadow *n.* A field of grass.
pond *n.* A small lake.
stump *n.* The part of a tree that is left after the tree has been cut down.
disguise *n.* Something that hides the way one looks.

Practice **Circle the vocabulary word in parentheses that matches each definition below.**

1. A small lake (pond, hare)

2. Something that hides the way one looks (scent, disguise)

3. A kind of rabbit (hare, stump)

4. A field of grass (disguise, meadow)

5. The part of a tree that is left after the tree has been cut down (meadow, stump)

6. A smell (scent, pond)

Name _____ Date _____

Spelling: /o͞o/ spelled *u*, *u_e*, *_ew*, and *_ue*

Focus   The /o͞o/ sound sounds like the word *moo*. Some ways that the /o͞o/ sound can be spelled are:

u	t<u>u</u>ba
u_e	t<u>u</u>n<u>e</u>
_ew	kn<u>ew</u>
_ue	bl<u>ue</u>

Practice

blew	clue	June	due	dew	lure

Consonant-Substitution Strategy

Replace the underlined letter or letters to make a spelling word from the box.

1. <u>t</u>rue   +   cl   =   _____

2. <u>kn</u>ew   +   bl   =   _____

3. <u>s</u>ure   +   l   =   _____

4. <u>s</u>ue   +   d   =   _____

5. <u>n</u>ew   +   d   =   _____

6. <u>t</u>une   +   J   =   _____

Name _____ Date _____

Possessive Nouns and Possessive Pronouns

Focus   A **possessive noun** shows ownership.

Rule

- Add an apostrophe s ('s) to most singular nouns.

- Add an apostrophe (') to plural nouns that end in s.

- A possessive pronoun can be used instead of a possessive noun.

Possessive pronouns: *my, your, his, her, its, their,* and *our*

Example

- Jessica**'s** bicycle is red.

- The cat**s'** were on the floor.

- Luke**'s** dad is a firefighter.

- **His** dad is a firefighter.

Practice   **Rewrite each phrase using a possessive noun.**

1. the book that belongs to Alice _____

2. the car of my parents _____

Fill in the blank with a possessive pronoun.

_____ car is red.

Day 2

Name _____ Date _____

/oo/ Spelled oo

Focus
- Say the word *book*. This word has the /oo/ sound spelled *oo*.

Practice **Write a word from the box that rhymes.**

look	good	cook	wood

1. shook _____

2. hood _____

3. brook _____

4. stood _____

Circle the word that makes the oo sound.

1. look/loop

2. mood/wood

3. broom/brook

4. stood/stoop

5. foot/food

Phonics • *Reteach*

Name _____ Date _____

Prefixes *dis-* and *un-*

Focus A **prefix** is added to the beginning of a word to change the word's meaning.

- The prefix **dis-** means "not" or "opposite."

  Example   dis + like = dislike (to not like)

- The prefix **un-** means "not."

  Example   un + kind = unkind (not kind)

Practice **Add the prefix *dis-*, and then write what the word means.**

1. dis + respect = _____   meaning: _____

2. dis + agree = _____   meaning: _____

3. dis + connect = _____   meaning: _____

Add the prefix *un-*, and then write what the word means.

1. un + tie = _____

meaning: _____

2. un + done = _____   meaning: _____

3. un + known = _____   meaning: _____

Name _____ Date _____

Selection Vocabulary

Focus

| creatures | glides | fade |
| delay | designed | proceeds |

Practice Read each definition below. Circle the word that matches each definition.

1. To put off
  a. designed   **b.** delay   **c.** creatures

2. Past tense of design; to plan or make
  a. proceeds   **b.** glides   **c.** designed

3. To lose color or brightness
  a. fade   **b.** delay   **c.** glides

4. Plural of creature; a living thing
  a. fade   **b.** creatures   **c.** proceeds

5. Moves in a smooth way
  a. glides   **b.** fade   **c.** creatures

6. Moves on or continues
  a. glides   **b.** delay   **c.** proceeds

Selection Vocabulary • *Reteach*

Name _____ Date _____

Spelling: The /oo/ sound

Focus The /oo/ sound sounds like the word *hood.*

Practice **Meaning Strategy**
Circle the word in parentheses that best completes the sentence.

1. We gathered a large pile of (soot, wood) for our fireplace.

2. Can you walk by putting one (foot, stood) in front of the other?

3. Please hang your coat up on the (shook, hook).

4. The ripe apples tasted so (good, look).

5. The ground (stood, shook) during the earthquake.

Name _____ Date _____

Conjunctions and Compound Sentences

Focus

- **Conjunctions** connect words or groups of words in a sentence. Some conjunctions: *and, but, or.*
  Example
  > Lynn **and** Matthew are coming to visit Tuesday **or** Wednesday.

- A **compound sentence** uses a conjunction *(and, but, or)* to combine two simple sentences into one longer sentence.

  Example   Abby wanted ice cream. John wanted pie.

  Abby wanted ice cream **but** John wanted pie.

Practice   Circle the conjunctions in the sentences below.

1. A shark and a stingray swam by a group of swimmers.

2. The sea dragon has ribbons of skin on its chin, belly, and back.

Make the pair of sentences into a compound sentence using a conjunction *(and, but, or).*

Jacob likes horseshoe crabs. I like sand dollars.

_____

_____

Grammar • *Reteach*

Name _____ **Date** _____

/ow/ Spelled *ow, ou_*

Focus
• The **/ow/** sound can be spelled *ow*, as in the word *cow*. It can also be spelled *ou_*, as in the word *out*.

Practice
Write the words from the box into the correct column. Underline the letters that make the /ow/ sound in each word.

now	down	cloud	crowd	flower	sound
house	shout	noun	wow	loud	power

ow   **ou_**

_____   _____

_____   _____

_____   _____

_____   _____

_____   _____

Name _____ Date _____

Prefixes *mis-* and *mid-*

Focus
- A **prefix** is a word part that is added to the beginning of a base word to make a new word.
- The prefix **mis-** means "bad", "wrong", or "incorrectly".
  Example   mis + spell = misspell (to spell incorrectly)
- The prefix **mid-** means "middle".
  Example   mid + year = midyear (middle of the year)

 **Practice** **Add the prefix *mis-*, then write what the word means.**

1. mis + behave = _____   meaning: _____

2. mis + understand = _____

meaning: _____

Add the prefix *mid-*, then write what the word means.

1. mid + night = _____

meaning: _____

2. mid + way = _____

meaning: _____

Word Structure • *Reteach*

Name _____ Date _____

Selection Vocabulary

 **Focus**

glossy	bank	temper
reeds	delicate	admired

 **Practice**   **Fill in the blank with the vocabulary word in parentheses that best completes the sentence.**

1. There were many tall _____ (reeds, glossy) growing

along the river _____ (temper, bank).

2. The petals on a flower are very _____ (delicate, admired).

3. It can be hard to control your _____ (reeds, temper) when you are angry.

Replace the underlined word with a vocabulary word from the box.

1. Julia's hair looked <u>shiny</u> after she washed it. _____

2. I have always <u>thought well of</u> doctors for the hard work

they do. _____

Name _____ Date _____

Classify and Categorize

Focus
- Readers classify and categorize to help keep track of information in a story.

    Example   Art Supplies   School Supplies

    List the things, characters, or events that fit under each category.

    Example   <u>Art Supplies</u>   <u>School Supplies</u>

        crayons, paints,   scissors, pencils
        scissors, brushes   papers, crayons

Practice   **Circle the thing that does not fit into the category.**

1. Things to play with

    balls   stores   dolls   games

2. Things to eat

    apples   carrots   lamps   potatoes

3. Things with wheels

    dogs   bikes   cars   trucks

4. Things that drink water

    people   cats   dogs   books

Name _____ Date _____

Classify and Categorize

Look at the things in the box. List each thing under the correct category.

toothpaste	plates	shampoo	napkins
toothbrush	comb	forks	pots

Things you might find
in a bathroom:

_____

_____

_____

_____

Things you might find
in a kitchen:

_____

_____

_____

_____

Name _____ Date _____

Spelling: The /ow/ sound spelled *ow* and *ou*

Focus

The /ow/ sound sounds like the word *cow*. Two ways that the /ow/ sound can be spelled are:

ow	pl<u>ow</u>
ou	<u>ou</u>t

Practice

hour	loud	now	town	round	howl

Rhyming Strategy

Write the spelling word from the box that rhymes with each word below. The spelling word will have the same spelling for the /ow/ sound.

1. proud _____

2. found _____

3. growl _____

4. flour _____

5. how _____

6. brown _____

Name _____ Date _____

Synonyms and Antonyms

Focus
- A **synonym** is a word that has a similar meaning to another word.
  Example   happy   glad
- An **antonym** is a word that means the opposite of another word.
  Example   happy   sad

Practice **Read each sentence. Circle the word in parentheses that could replace the underlined word.**

1. The sun is very *bright* today. (shiny, big)

2. That building is sixty feet *tall*. (under, high)

3. Mrs. Harris is such a *friendly* teacher. (kind, smart)

Write a word from the box next to its antonym.

above	heavy	before	clean

1. after _____

2. below _____

3. dirty _____

4. light _____

Name _____ Date _____

Review: /o͞o/, /oo/, and /ow/

Focus

- /o͞o/ can be spelled **oo, u, u_e, _ew, and ue.**
- /oo/ can be spelled **oo,** as in the word *book.*
- /**ow**/ can be spelled *ow,* as in the word *cow,* or *ou_,* as in the word *shout.*

Practice   Underline the spelling for the /o͞o/ sound in each word.

1. noon   **3.** flew   **5.** duty

2. true   **4.** tune

Write a word that rhymes with each /oo/ word below.

1. good _____   **2.** cook _____

Write a word that rhymes with each /ow/ word below.

1. mouse _____   **2.** proud _____

Name _____ Date _____

Inflectional Endings, Comparative Endings, and Irregular Plurals

Focus

- **Inflectional endings** are word parts that are added to the end of a base word. They change the form but they do not change the meaning of the word.

  -ing and *-ed* are **inflectional endings**.
- The **comparative ending -er** shows a comparison between two things.
- **Irregular plurals** are words that do not become plural by adding -s or -es.

Practice **Circle the word in parentheses that best completes the sentence.**

1. We enjoyed (watched, watching) the football game on T.V.

2. Rob (looked, looking) for his watch all morning.

Complete the sentence below with a word that makes sense.

1. A house is **larger** than a _____

Draw a line to match each plural to its singular form.

Plural	Singular
men	knife
geese	man
knives	goose

Name _____ Date _____

Selection Vocabulary

Focus | natural   unaware   available
protective   coloration   imitator

Practice   Circle the word that goes with the definition.

1. Keeps out of danger or away from harm
     a. coloration   **b.** natural   **c.** protective

2. One who copies something or someone
     a. imitator   **b.** unaware   **c.** protective

3. The way something is colored
     a. available   **b.** coloration   **c.** unaware

Choose the word in parentheses that best completes the sentence. Write the word on the line.

1. The mouse was _____ that the snake was watching it. (unaware, available)

2. There were no seats _____ when we got to the theater. (available, protective)

3. It is _____ to feel nervous when you start a new school. (protective, natural)

     Selection Vocabulary • *Reteach*

Name _____ Date _____

Spelling: Review

Focus

blue	frown	books
scout	cookie	cool

Practice **Visualization Strategy**
Circle the correctly spelled word in each pair below. Then write the word on the line.

1. scowt   scout   _____

2. cookie   cooky   _____

3. blue   bleu   _____

4. kule   cool   _____

5. froun   frown   _____

6. books   boocz   _____

Name _____ **Date** _____

Colons

Copyright © SRA/McGraw-Hill. Permission is granted to reproduce this page for classroom use.

Focus A **colon (:)** is a type of punctuation mark.

• Colons are used to introduce a list.

• Colons are also used to separate the hour and the minutes when writing the time.

Practice **Write the time using numerals and a colon.**

Example   Five-thirty = 5:30

1. Six-twenty _____

3. Four-fifteen _____

2. Eleven o'clock _____

Write the colon in the correct place.

1. Dinner starts at 6 00.

2. Please bring the following items on our camping trip toothbrush, flashlight, sleeping bag, and pillow.

Finish the sentences with a colon and a list of 3 things that make sense.

1. When school starts, you will need to bring the following supplies

_____

Grammar • *Reteach*

Name _____ Date _____

/aw/ spelled *au_* and *aw*

Focus
- The sound **/aw/** can be spelled *au_*, as in the word *haul.* It can also be spelled *aw,* as in the word *awful.*

Practice **Write the words from the box in the correct column.**

strawberry	sauce	author	claw	laundry	saw

*au_* words	*aw* words
_____	_____
_____	_____

Write the two words from the box that rhyme.

_____   _____

Circle the word in parentheses that best completes the sentence.

1. Most babies (crawl, claws) before they learn to walk.

2. During a (paws, pause) in the test, I got a drink of water.

Name _____ Date _____

Suffixes -er and -ness

Focus
- A **suffix** is added to the end of a word.
- The suffix -er changes a word so that it means "one who"
- The suffix -**ness** changes a word so that it means "the state of being"

Practice Add the suffix -er, then write what the word means.

1. sing + er   =   _____   meaning: _____

2. play + er   =   _____   meaning: _____

Add the suffix -ness, then write what the word means.

1. sick + ness   =   _____

meaning: _____

2. thankful + ness   =   _____

meaning: _____

Name _____ Date _____

Selection Vocabulary

Focus

brave	puffing	leaping
avalanche	trembling	afraid

Practice Circle the word that best completes the sentence.

1. While we were skiing, we saw an (avalanche, afraid).

2. After I went running, I was huffing and (puffing, trembling).

3. You must be (leaping, brave) to be a lion tamer.

4. We saw frogs (leaping, trembling) across the lily pads at the pond.

5. Many children sleep with a nightlight because they are (afraid, brave) of the dark.

6. Kim was (leaping, trembling) after playing out in the snow too long.

Write a sentence about a time that you were _brave_.

_____

_____

Name _____ Date _____

Spelling: The /aw/ sound spelled *aw* and *au_*

Focus

The /aw/ sound sounds like the word *law*. It can be spelled:

aw   cl<u>aw</u>

*au_*   h<u>au</u>l

Practice

| sauce | thaw | launch | yawn | cause | hawk |

Meaning Strategy

Choose the spelling word from the box that best completes the sentence.

1. Our class got to watch the space shuttle _____ on Friday.

2. Were the firefighters able to determine the _____ of the fire?

3. May I please have tomato _____ on my spaghetti?

4. The _____ circled around the sky throughout the afternoon.

5. The frozen beef has to _____ before we can cook it.

6. By the end of the school day, I was so tired I began to _____.

Spelling • *Reteach*

Name _____ Date _____

Capitalization and Commas in Greetings and Closings of Letters

Focus

- A letter usually begins with the word *Dear* and is followed by the name of the person receiving the letter. The word *Dear* is always capitalized.

- The first word of a closing in a letter is also capitalized.

- In the greeting, the comma is placed after the name of the person receiving the letter.

- In the closing, a comma is placed between the closing word or phrase and the author's signature.

Practice Decide if the greetings and closings have the correct capitalization. Circle yes or no. Then, cross out the incorrect letter and write the correct one above it.

1. very truly yours,   yes   no

2. Dear Melissa,   yes   no

3. dear mom,   yes   no

4. Your Friend,   yes   no

Name _____ **Date** _____

/aw/ Spelled augh, ough, all, and al

Focus

- We have already reviewed two spellings for the sound **/aw/: au_ and aw.** The **/aw/** sound can also be spelled:

augh, as in the word **taught**

ough, as in the word **thought**

all, as in the word **small**

al, as in the word **walk**

Practice Write the word from the box that rhymes. The word will have the same spelling of the /aw/ sound.

fought	walk	caught	salt	call

1. chalk _____

2. ball _____

3. halt _____

4. bought _____

5. taught _____

Phonics • *Reteach*

Name _____ Date _____

Suffixes *-ly, -y,* and *-ed*

Focus
- A **suffix** is added to the end of a base word.
- The suffix *-ly* means "in a certain way."
- The suffix *-y* means "full of."
- The suffix *-ed* shows that something has already happened. It changes the tense of the word from present to past.
- When a base word has a short vowel followed by a consonant, the consonant is usually doubled before adding *-ed.*

Practice Add the suffix *-ly* to the following words. Then, write the meaning of the new word.

1. quick + ly = _____ meaning: _____

2. soft + ly = _____ meaning: _____

Add the suffix *-y* to the following words. Then write the meaning of the new word.

1. dirt + y = _____ meaning: _____

2. wind + y = _____ meaning: _____

Add the suffix *-ed* to the following words. Remember to double the final consonant.

1. step + ed = _____

2. shop + ed = _____

Name _____ Date _____

Selection Vocabulary

Focus

windmills	dikes	flooded
trickling	numb	rumbling

Practice **Circle the correct definition of the boldfaced word.**

1. I could feel the rain **trickling** down my face. **Trickling** means:
   a. having no feeling   **b.** flowing drop by drop

2. The town was **flooded** when the river overflowed. **Flooded** means:
   a. covered with water   **b.** making a heavy, deep, rolling sound

3. We could hear the thunder **rumbling** in the distance. **Rumbling** means:
   a. flowing drop by drop   **b.** making a heavy, deep, rolling sound

4. My legs were **numb** after sitting on the floor for too long. **Numb** means:
   a. having no feeling   **b.** covered with water

Draw a line to match each word to its definition on the right.

1. dikes   **a.** machines that use wind power

2. windmills   **b.** thick walls built to hold back water

Selection Vocabulary • *Reteach*

Name _____ Date _____

Cause and Effect

> **Focus** Seeing cause and effect relationships between the events in a story will help a reader understand the story better.
>
> A **cause** is *why* something happens.
>
> An **effect** is *what* happens.
>
> Because some animals blend into their surroundings, **(Cause)** they are hard to see. **(Effect)**

Practice **For each sentence below, circle the cause and underline the effect.**

1. I visited the doctor because I had a sore throat.

2. Everyone was in the car, so we were ready to go.

3. The dog started barking because he heard a noise.

4. I don't like pink lemonade, so I drank water.

5. Marvin went back inside because he forgot his lunch.

6. Catherine couldn't keep her eyes open, so she went to bed.

7. My dad drove me to school because I missed the bus.

8. The store was closed, so we had to go to another store.

Name _____ **Date** _____

Read each sentence. Write the effect and the cause.

9. I wore my jacket because it was chilly outside.

Effect: _____

Cause: _____

10. Because it was his birthday, we baked a cake.

Effect: _____

Cause: _____

11. The deer hid when he smelled the hunters.

Effect: _____

Cause: _____

12. It's hot today, so we're going for a swim.

Effect: _____

Cause: _____

Finish the sentence below. Add an effect.

Jackie wanted to play baseball

_____

Comprehension • *Reteach*

Name _____ Date _____

Spelling: The /aw/ sound spelled *augh,* *ough, all,* and *al*

Focus   The /aw/ sound sounds like the word *law.* Some ways that the /aw/ sound can be spelled are:

augh	<u>daugh</u>ter
ough	<u>fough</u>t
all	t<u>all</u>
al	t<u>al</u>k

Practice

walk	bought	call	taught	haltt	caught

Visualization Strategy
Circle the correctly spelled word. Then write the word on the line.

1. taught   tallt   _____

2. caughl   call   _____

3. houghlt   halt   _____

4. walk   wallk   _____

5. balt   bought   _____

6. cought   caught   _____

Name _____ **Date** _____

Quotation Marks

Focus

- **Quotation Marks** are used to indicate dialogue. Dialogue tells the reader exactly what the characters say.

- Put quotation marks (" ") before and after a speaker's exact words.

- Quotation marks are also used to indicate the titles of stories, songs, and poems.

Practice   **Add quotation marks where they are needed.**

1. Did you remember your glasses? asked the teacher.

2. My sister and I wrote a story together called   The Amazing Mystery.

Put quotation marks before and after the speaker's words, and around titles of stories, songs, and poems.

- My brother said,

_____

- Have you heard the song?

_____

    Grammar • *Reteach*

Name _____ Date _____

The *ough* spelling pattern

Focus
- The spelling pattern **ough** has many different sounds.
- The /aw/ sound when the letter *t* is added to the end of *ough*
- The long o sound, as in the word *dough*
- The short u sound, as in the word *enough*
- The /$\overline{oo}$/ sound, as in the word *through*

Practice Write each word from the box in the correct column according to its sound.

dough	through	rough	thought
/**aw**/	Long o	Short u	/$\overline{oo}$/
_____	_____	_____	_____

Circle the word in parentheses that best completes the sentence.

Did you get (rough, enough) to eat?

Name _____ Date _____

Suffixes -*less* and -*ful*
Prefixes and Suffixes as Syllables

Focus

- The suffix **-less** means "without".
- The suffix **-ful** means "full of".
- **Suffixes**, which are added to the end of words, and **prefixes**, which are added to the beginning of words, add a syllable to base words.

Example   The word "like" has one syllable.

Adding the suffix -*ly* makes the word "likely", which has two syllables: like•ly.

Adding the prefix -*un* to the word "likely" makes the word "unlikely", which has three syllables: un•like•ly

Practice   Add the suffix to the words below. Then, write the meaning of the new word.

1. care + less = _____   meaning: _____

2. help + ful = _____   meaning: _____

Divide each word below into syllables by circling each syllable.

1. dis•a•gree   **2.** sing•er

Word Structure • *Reteach*

Name _____ Date _____

Selection Vocabulary

Focus

kingdom	emperor	tended	
sprout	blossom	transferred	courage

Practice Circle the vocabulary word that best completes the sentence.

1. I could see a green (sprout, kingdom) a few days after we planted our seed. We (transferred, tended) to it with loving care. In another week, the flower began to (blossom, emperor).

2. After my family moved, I (transferred, tended) to a new school. It took real (kingdom, courage) to begin to make new friends there.

Circle the correct definition for the vocabulary word.

1. "Kingdom" means:

a. To begin to grow   **b.** A country ruled by a king or queen

2. "Emperor" means:

a. A ruler   **b.** To take care of

Write a sentence using the words *kingdom* and *emperor*.

_____

_____

Name _____ Date _____

Spelling: Sounds for *ough*

Focus The *ough* spelling can make many different sounds:

The /aw/ sound, as in the word *cough*.

The long o sound, as in the word *dough*.

The /u/ sound, as in the word *tough*.

Practice

| fought | rough | though | cough | tough | dough |

Write each spelling word from the box under the correct sound heading below.

/aw/	long o	short u
1. _____	1. _____	1. _____
2. _____	2. _____	2. _____

Name _____ Date _____

Commas in Dialogue

Focus

Rule

A **comma** (,) separates the quotation marks from the rest of the sentence. If the quotation is at the beginning of the sentence, the comma goes after the last word and before the end quotation marks. If the quotation is at the end of the sentence, the comma goes before the quotation begins.

Examples

"Let's go camping**,**" said LaShauna.

Jessica asked**,** "Where should we go camping?"

Practice **Put commas where they belong in each sentence.**

1. "My rabbit eats lettuce" said Vicki.

2. Wilbur asked "Does he like carrots?"

Put commas where they belong in each sentence. Put an X through any commas used incorrectly.

3. "My rabbit's name is Gregory" said Sarah.

4. Alyssa, asked "Do rabbits make good pets?"

Name _____ Date _____

/oi/ spelled oi, _oy

Focus • The /oi/ sound can be spelled **oi**, as in the word **join**. It can also be spelled **_oy**, as in the word **toy**.

Practice Write the word from the box that rhymes with each word below. The word will have the same spelling of the /oi/ sound.

foil	coin	joy	loyal

1. boy _____

3. royal _____

2. join _____

4. toil _____

In each sentence below, circle the words with the /oi/ sound. Then, underline the spelling for /oi/ in each word.

1. Each spring, Laura toils for hours planting flowers in the soil.

2. I lost my voice at the ballgame because I had to shout over all the noise.

3. I think I would enjoy being a cowboy.

4. Joy always makes such moist cakes.

5. Did you make a choice about which toy you wanted?

Name _____ Date _____

Homographs and Homophones

Focus
- **Homographs** are words that are spelled and pronounced the same but have different meanings.

  Example

  The Red Sox fan brought a little fan to the game in the summer.

- **Homophones** are words that sound the same, but have different spelling and meanings.

  Example

  Did you hear me say to come here?

Practice **Write the word on the line next to both of its definitions.**

1. An insect
Something birds and airplanes can do _____

Write the word from the box that completes the homophone pair.

too	blue	pear	sun

1. blew _____

2. pair _____

3. two _____

4. son _____

Name _____ **Date** _____

Selection Vocabulary

Focus

| rugged | snapped | shifted | burrowed |
| snowdrift | squinted | rumble | |

Practice   **Circle the word in the parentheses that best completes the sentence.**

1. The baby _____ in the bright sun. (squinted, snowdrift)

2. Last night, we heard a _____ of thunder before the storm began. (snapped, rumble)

3. A family of rabbits _____ under the ground. (burrowed, rugged)

4. We couldn't leave our house last winter after a huge _____ blocked our driveway. (rumble, snowdrift)

Circle the word in parentheses that goes with the underlined definition in each sentence.

1. The road through the mountains was very rough and uneven. (rugged, shifted)

2. The pitcher moved quickly and sharply the ball to the catcher. (shifted, snapped)

3. Mom changed position of the baby to her other hip. (shifted, rugged)

    Selection Vocabulary • *Reteach*

Name _____ Date _____

Sequence

Focus

Knowing when things happen in a story and the order in which things happen can help you understand the story.

Sequence means the order in which things happen in a story. Here are examples of time and order words that help show the sequence in a story:

Today, yesterday, once upon a time, first, then, later, finally, next

Practice **Read the sentences. Underline the time and order words in each sentence.**

1. Today is my dog's birthday.

2. Did you get the newspaper yesterday?

3. I want to go shopping later.

4. First, let's get an ice cream cone.

5. Then, we are going on a field trip.

6. Finally, I put on my coat.

Name _____ **Date** _____

Use the words in the box below to complete the sentences.

tomorrow	yesterday	today

1. Gretchen is coming _____ to pick up the cat.

2. The books are due _____.

3. It was foggy _____.

Number the following sentences in the order in which they happen. Circle the order words.

1. _____ Finally, the show began.

2. _____ First, we found our seats at the circus.

3. _____ Next, we watched the spotlights start to flash.

Write a sentence using one of the words below.

today	yesterday

_____

_____

Comprehension • *Reteach*

Name _____ Date _____

Spelling: The /oi/ sound spelled *oi* and *_oy*

Focus

The /oi/ sound sounds like the word *moist.* It can be spelled:

oi   br<u>oi</u>l

_oy   j<u>oy</u>

Practice

| spoil | choice | boys | coin | toy |

Rhyming Strategy

Choose the spelling word from the box that rhymes with each word below. The spelling word will have the same spelling for the /oi/ sound.

1. joys _____

2. join _____

3. voice _____

4. boil _____

5. coy _____

Name _____ **Date** _____

Adverbs

Focus

- An **adverb** describes a verb. Adverbs can tell *when, where,* or *how*. Many adverbs that answer *how* end in *-ly*.

Examples

The fox ran **quickly**. (how?)

Our cat ran **away**. (where?)

I will talk to you **later**. (when?)

Practice   **Read each sentence. Underline the adverb.**

1. My little sister wakes up early.

2. The summer days passed by slowly.

3. We can play outside.

4. Wow! You can run fast!

Complete each sentence with an adverb that answers the questions.

1. When? Meet me _____

2. How? Andrea swam _____

Grammar • *Reteach*

Name _____ Date _____

Review: /aw/ and /oi/

 **Focus**
- The /aw/ sound can be spelled **aw, au_, augh, ough, all,** and **al.**
- The /oi/ sound can be spelled **oi** and **_oy.**

Practice Circle the words that have the /aw/ sound. Then, underline the spelling for the /aw/ sound in each word.

1. Jill thought she could walk all the way home.

2. I felt awful because it was my fault.

3. Grandpa taught me how to use a saw.

Circle the words that have the /oi/ sound. Then, underline the spelling for the /oi/ sound in each word.

1. My little sister enjoys annoying me by taking my toys.

2. Could you point out our choices for dinner?

3. Charlie joined the other boys in digging up the soil.

Name _____ **Date** _____

Related Words and Word Families

> **Focus**
> - Knowing how words are **related** can help you figure out word meanings.
>
>   plant   flower   daisy
>
> The words are **related** in this way: A daisy is a type of flower. A flower is a type of plant.
>
> - A **base word** is a word that can stand alone. It gives you a clue to the meaning of other words in its family.
>
> **Base Word:** rain
>
> **Base Word Family Members:** raindrop raincoat rainbow

Practice **Write how the words are related.**

animal   mammal   cat   calico

_____

_____

Using sun as a base, write other words from the family.

sun _____

Name _____ Date _____

Selection Vocabulary

Focus

| reservation | dreaded | stomping | inform |
| qualified | mountain lion | mysterious | |

Practice Fill in the blank with a vocabulary word from the box. Hint: the first letter is printed for you as a clue.

1. We saw several tepees on the Cherokee **r** _____.

2. Coach Jenkins was **q** _____ to teach diving.

3. A cougar is another name for a **m** _____

 l _____.

4. Mary **d** _____ the big math test on Friday.

5. Steven liked **s** _____ in the puddles with his new boots.

6. There was a **m** _____ glow in the sky last night.

7. Mom had to **i** _____ Mrs. Miller that I would be absent next week.

Name _____ **Date** _____

Author's Purpose

Focus **Writers have different reasons for writing.**

Writers write to **inform.**
- Includes facts and information that can be proven

Writers write to **entertain.**
- Includes funny words or exciting events

Writers write to **persuade.**
- Includes opinions and facts that support opinions

Practice **Tell if the sentences were written to *entertain*
or to *inform*.**

1. There are eight planets. The one farthest from Earth is called Neptune.

   These sentences were written to _____.

2. Robbie didn't know what to do when the cow said to him, "Why don't you have a glass of milk? It will make you feel better."

   These sentences were written to _____.

Name _____ **Date** _____

In the box are purposes for writing. Read each story title, and then choose the best purpose for each story. Write the purpose on the line.

inform	entertain	persuade

1. How to Make Spaghetti _____

2. Facts about Fish _____

3. Frogs Are Better Pets Than Snakes _____

4. The Great Snake Escape _____

5. How to Make a Peanut Butter and Jelly Sandwich

_____

Name _____ **Date** _____

Spelling: Review

 **lawn   recall   stalk   naughty   thoughts   oyster   noise**

Practice **Visualization Strategy**
Circle the correctly spelled word in each pair below.
Then, write the word on the line.

1. notty   naughty   _____

2. oyster   oistir   _____

3. lawn   laun   _____

4. noyz   noise   _____

5. recall   recoughl   _____

6. thotz   thoughts   _____

7. staughk   stalk   _____

Name _____ Date _____

Verb Tenses

Focus

A **verb** can show that something is happening in the present, happened in the past, or will happen in the future.

- A **verb** that tells what is happening now is a **present tense verb**.

- A **verb** that tells what happened in the past is a **past tense verb**.

- A **verb** that tells what will happen in the future is a **future tense verb**.

- Most verbs change from present to past tense by adding -**ed** to the end of the verb.

Practice

Change the following verb from present to past tense by adding -ed.

1. walk _____

2. open _____

3. look _____

Name _____ **Date** _____

Review: /o͞o/, /ow/, /ō/, /ū/, and /o͝o/

Focus

- The spelling **ow** can make the /ō/ sound, as in the word low. It can also make the /**ow**/ sound, as in the word **cow**.

- The spellings **u, ew, ue, and u_e** can make the /o͞o/ sound, as in the words **truth, new, blue,** and **June.** They can also make the /**ū**/ sound, as in the words **use, few, cue,** and **cube**.

- Words that have the **oo** spelling can have two sounds: /o͞o/, as in the word **cool,** and /o͝o/, as in the word **book**.

Practice Circle the correct sound for each word in bold.

1. Our desks are in **rows**.
/ō/   /ow/

2. Tell me the **truth**.
/ū/   /o͞o/

3. Do you take a bus to **school**?
/o͝o/   /o͞o/

4. Daisies are my favorite **flower**.
/ō/   /ow/

5. Grandma Betty is a great **cook**.
/o͝o/   /o͞o/

6. A **cube** has square faces.
/ū/   /o͞o/

Phonics · *Reteach*

Name _____ Date _____

Antonyms and Synonyms

Focus **Antonyms** are words that mean the opposite of another word.

Synonyms are words that mean the same as or almost the same as another word.

Practice **Circle the antonym of the boldfaced word.**

1. This will be our **last** night of vacation.
first   middle

2. Sam was **late** to the birthday party.
last   early

3. The baby was **asleep** during the car ride.
awake   tired

Replace the underlined word with one from the box.

cap	hot	jump

1. I wore a <u>hat</u> to the game. _____

2. In July, it is often <u>warm</u>. _____

3. The rabbit will <u>hop</u> over to me. _____

Name _____ Date _____

Selection Vocabulary

Focus   orchid   sesame   explorer   discovered

chores   popular   wiser

Practice   Circle the correct definition for the boldfaced word.

1. One of my weekly **chores** is taking out the trash.
   a. small jobs around the house   **b.** a type of flower

2. Root beer is a **popular** drink.
   a. smarter   **b.** liked or accepted by many people.

3. Last week, I **discovered** an old coin buried in my yard.
   a. a person who travels to a new place for the purpose of discovery
   b. be the first to find, learn of, or observe

4. I like sandwiches made on **sesame** seed buns.
   a. a type of flower
   b. a tropical Asian plant bearing small, flat seeds used as food and as a source of oil.

5. Christopher Columbus was an **explorer** to the new world.
   a. a person who travels to a new place for the purpose of discovery
   b. liked or accepted by many people.

Selection Vocabulary • *Reteach*

Name _____ Date _____

Fact and Opinion

Focus A story can include both facts and opinions about things or people. Story characters can have opinions, too.

- A **fact** can be checked and proven true. It *is a fact that fish can swim.*

- An **opinion** cannot be proven. It is one person's idea. It is *an opinion when someone says they don't like fish.*

Practice A Write whether the sentence gives a fact or an opinion.

1. _____ Fruits are the best food.

2. _____ Tomatoes are usually red when ripe.

3. _____ There are many ways to cook potatoes.

4. _____ Children should be taught to cook.

5. _____ Ice cream is the best dessert.

6. _____ Oranges and lemons are fruits.

7. _____ Bananas grow on trees.

8. _____ Everyone loves peanut butter and jelly sandwiches.

Name _____ Date _____

Fact and Opinion

Practice B Draw a line under each sentence that tells a fact. Circle the sentences that give opinions.

    Cooking is a lot of fun. Some people are chefs. Their job is to cook. Many chefs go to cooking school. Both men and women can be chefs. Home cooking is better than a chef's cooking. Hotels, restaurants, schools, and even airlines have chefs. It would be a fun job to be a chef.

Write a sentence that gives an opinion about your favorite cereal.

_____

_____

Name _____ Date _____

Contrast /ō/, /ow/, / o͞o/, /ū/, and /oo/

Focus

The *ow* spelling can make two different sounds:

/ō/, as in the word *know*.

/ow/, as in the word *growl*.

The *u_e* spelling can make two different sounds:

/o͞o/, as in the word *tube*.

/ū/, as in the word *cube*.

The *oo* spelling can make two different sounds:

/o͞o/, as in the word *moon*.

/oo/, as in the word *good*.

Practice

| flow | cook | loom | flower |

Rhyming Strategy
Choose the spelling word from the box that rhymes with each word below.

1. book _____

2. power _____

3. room _____

4. grow _____

Reteach • Spelling

Name _____ Date _____

Common and Proper Nouns
Action, Linking, and Helping Verbs

Focus

- A **common noun** names a general person, place, or thing.

- A **proper noun** names a particular person, place, or thing. Proper nouns begin with a capital letter.

- An **action verb** is the word in a sentence that tells what is happening.

- A **linking verb** joins parts of sentences to make them complete. They *do not* show action.

- A **helping verb** is used with an action verb to help tell when something is happening.

Practice **Underline the proper nouns in the sentence. Circle the common nouns.**

1. Roberto and Michelle walked down the street to get ice cream.

Underline the action verb in each sentence.

1. Dad drove me to baseball practice.

Read the following sentences. Write on the line if the underlined word is a *linking* or *helping* verb.

1. Gloria <u>is</u> cleaning her room. _____

2. My mom <u>was</u> a drummer in high school. _____

Grammar • *Reteach*

Name _____ Date _____

Silent Letters

Focus Silent letters are consonants in words that cannot be heard when the word is read. Examples of letters that can be silent are: *w, h, c, g, t, b.*

Practice **Underline the silent letter in each word below.**

1. crumb   **5.** answer

2. gnat   **6.** scissors

3. ghost   **7.** reign

4. fasten

Underline the word with a silent letter in each sentence below.

1. Karen answered the question.

2. Did you pet the lamb at the farm?

3. I walked to school this morning.

4. My favorite scene is coming up.

5. Listen carefully to the directions.

Name _____ Date _____

Prefixes: *dis-*, *un-*, *mis-*, and *mid-*

Focus

- A **prefix** is a part that is added to the beginning of a base word to make a new word. Adding a prefix changes the meaning of the word.
- The prefix **dis-** means "not" or "opposite"
- The prefix **un-** means "not"
- The prefix **mis-** means "bad" or "wrong"
- The prefix **mid-** means "middle"

Practice Add the prefix to the base word to form a new word. Then, write the meaning of the word on the line below.

1. dis + honest = _____ meaning: _____

2. un + happy = _____ meaning: _____

3. mis + place = _____ meaning: _____

4. mid + night = _____ meaning: _____

Word Structure • *Reteach*

Name _____ Date _____

Selection Vocabulary

Focus

recycling	adopted	doe	shed
brisk	fabric	leather	citizens

Practice Circle the answer that matches the definition.

1. Material made from animal skin
  a. shed   **b.** leather

2. To take as one's own
  a. adopt   **b.** doe

3. A person who was born in or chooses to live in a country
  a. citizen   **b.** fabric

4. A female deer
  a. leather   **b.** doe

5. A small building used for storing things
  a. shed   **b.** doe

6. Using throwaway items for another purpose
  a. adopted   **b.** recycling

7. Quick and lively
  a. brisk   **b.** shed

8. Cloth
  a. doe   **b.** fabric

Name _____ Date _____

Cause and Effect

Focus Looking for causes and effects helps you better understand story events.

- A **cause** is why something happens.
- An **effect** is what happens as a result.

Practice A Read each sentence below. Then answer the questions. The first one is done for you.

1. My boot was wet because I stepped in a puddle.

What happened? <u>My boot was wet.</u>

Why did it happen? <u>I stepped in a puddle.</u>

2. Courtney did well on the test because she studied.

What happened? _____

Why did it happen? _____

3. I laughed at the clown's magic trick.

What happened? _____

Why did it happen? _____

Comprehension • **Reteach**

Name _____ Date _____

Cause and Effect

Write the effect (what happened) and the cause (why the effect happened) in each sentence below.

1. I visited my grandmother because it was her birthday.

Effect: _____

Cause: _____

2. The game was canceled because of the bad weather.

Effect: _____

Cause: _____

3. I drank a glass of water because I was thirsty.

Effect: _____

Cause: _____

4. The flowers we planted last spring were pretty, so we planted them again.

Effect: _____

Cause: _____

Name _____ **Date** _____

Spelling: Silent Letters

Focus Silent letters are consonants in words that are not heard when the word is pronounced.

Examples

know, wrong

 | island   listen   rhino   whistle   answer   could

Visualization Strategy

Read each pair of words below. Circle the correctly spelled word. Then write the word on the line. Underline the silent letter in each word.

1. wissle   whistle   _____

2. answer   ancer   _____

3. island   eyeland   _____

4. cood   could   _____

5. listen   lisin   _____

6. rino   rhino   _____

Name _____ Date _____

Types of Sentences, Sentence Capitalization, and Punctuation

Focus

- A sentence begins with a **capital letter** and ends with a **period (.), question mark (?),** or an **exclamation point (!).**

- **Declarative sentences** make a statement and end in a period.

- **Interrogative sentences** ask a question and end in a question mark.

- **Imperative sentences** give a command and end in a period.

- **Exclamatory sentences** show great feeling or emotion and end in an exclamation point.

Practice | **Write what kind of sentence each is on the line. Write a capital letter or punctuation if needed.**

1. friction is a topic we studied in science.

_____

2. What is friction? _____

3. Friction is a force caused by two things rubbing together.

_____

4. without friction you couldn't walk!

_____

Name _____ Date _____

Three-letter consonant blends

Focus Consonants are blended when two or more consonants appear together in a word and each consonant keeps its own sound. Examples of three-letter consonant blends: *str-, scr-, spr, spl*

Practice Underline the consonant blend in each word.

1. scribble

2. strong

3. splinter

4. spring

5. string

6. splash

Circle the word that best completes each sentence.

1. My little brother (scraped, splintered) his knee on the sidewalk.

2. The beans were just beginning to (spray, sprout).

3. I heard the clock (strap, strike) midnight.

4. Marcy (sprawled, splashed) in the pool all day.

Phonics • *Reteach*

Name _____ Date _____

Inflectional Endings: *-ed, -ing*

Focus | Inflectional endings change the form or function of a word. They do not change the meaning of a word.

Base Word	**-ed**	**-ing**
Jump	jumped	jumping

Practice | Add *-ed* and *-ing* to each of the following verbs.

Verb	Add *-ed*	Add *-ing*
1. talk	_____	_____
2. pick	_____	_____
3. check	_____	_____

Circle the correct form of the verb in each sentence below.

1. Maria (wished, wishing) she could go to the party.

2. The monkey was (climbing, climbed) up the tree.

3. Kyle was (bounced, bouncing) on the trampoline.

Name _____ Date _____

Selection Vocabulary

 **Focus**   demanding   fair   laws   graduated
arrested   section   content   prejudice

Practice   Circle the correct definition for the vocabulary word in bold.

1. We took turns to make the game **fair.**
   a. not favoring one more than another
   b. unfair treatment of a group of people

2. Brian **graduated** from high school last year.
   a. to hold by authority of law
   b. to finish school

3. If you don't follow the traffic **laws,** you could cause an accident.
   a. rules made by the government
   b. a part

4. The bank robber was **arrested** and taken to jail.
   a. to finish school
   b. to hold by authority of law

5. The football fans were **demanding** tickets to the big game.
   a. asking for forcefully
   b. Unfair treatment of a group of people

Name _____ Date _____

Three-Letter Consonant Blends

Focus Say the word *stripe*. The letters *s, t,* and *r* make their own sounds, but they are said so quickly that the sounds blend together. Three-letter blends, such as *str, spr, scr,* and *spl,* are often found at the beginnings of words.

Practice

sprout	split	strange	scream	scratch	straw

Meaning Strategy
Read each sentence below. Choose the spelling word from the box that best completes the sentence.

1. We let out a loud _____ when the roller coaster went over the hill.

2. The watermelon seeds that we planted should _____ in June.

3. I like to sip my drinks through a _____.

4. Our cat will _____ on the door when she wants to come inside.

5. There was a _____ noise coming from the old building.

6. Would you like to _____ an apple with me?

Reteach • Spelling

Name _____ Date _____

Capitalization Rules: Proper Nouns, Titles, Initials, Days, Months, Cities, and States

The following items being with a capital letter:

- **Proper nouns**: A proper noun names a *particular* person, place, or thing, such as the **O**lympics

- **Titles** come before a person's name: **M**rs. Stewart

- A person's **initials: E.B.** White

- **Days of the week**: **M**onday

- **Months of the Year**: **J**anuary

- **Cities** and **States**: **C**olumbus, **O**hio

Practice Rewrite the following items using the correct capitalization.

1. sally jones _____

2. dr. anderson _____

3. c.s. lewis _____

4. wednesday _____

5. february _____

6. dallas, texas _____

Grammar • *Reteach*

Name _____ Date _____

The /ow/ and /aw/ Sounds

Focus
- The /**ow**/ sound can be spelled **ow**, as in the word **cow**. It can also be spelled **ou_**, as in the word **shout**.
- The /**aw**/ sound can be spelled **aw**, as in the word **saw**. It can also be spelled **au_**, as in the word **haul**.

Practice Underline the spelling of /ow/ in each word.

1. about   **2.** crown

Underline the spelling of /aw/ in each word.

1. because   **2.** straw

Write on the line whether the boldfaced word has the /ow/ or the /aw/ sound.

1. The **ground** was covered with leaves. _____

2. I like the **clowns** at the circus. _____

3. The baby is still learning to **crawl**. _____

4. Tomato **sauce** tastes good on spaghetti. _____

Name _____ **Date** _____

Suffixes: *-ly, -y, -less,* and *-ful*

Focus
- A **suffix** is a word part that is added to the end of a base word to make a new word.
- The suffix *-ly* means "in a certain way"
- The suffix *-y* means "full of"
- The suffix *-less* means "without"
- The suffix *-ful* means "full of"

 **Circle the word in parentheses that best completes the sentence.**

1. My sister's room was very (messy, messful).

2. Dad's car was (shineless, shiny) after he waxed it.

3. I had to correct the (careless, careful) mistakes on my paper.

4. Pet the kitten (softful, softly).

5. Andrea was (hopeless, hopeful) that she would win the election.

6. We ran (quickly, quickful) to get out of the rain.

7. Having your haircut is (painful, painless).

8. What a (beautiful, beautily) dress!

Word Structure • *Reteach*

Name _____ Date _____

Selection Vocabulary

Focus

calves	glimpse	strolled	pale
shuffled	pounding	slipped	ached

Practice Circle the word in parentheses that makes the most sense in the sentence.

1. Melanie (slipped, strolled) along the sidewalk to the store.

2. My heart was (pounding, ached) by the end of the race.

3. Her room was a (pounding, pale) shade of pink.

4. Sean caught a (glimpse, slipped) of the beautiful sunset.

Circle the definition that makes the most sense for the boldfaced word.

1. Mr. Edwards **shuffled** along behind the rest of the group.
Shuffled means:
a. to hurt with a dull, steady pain
b. to drag the feet while walking

2. Gymnasts must have very strong **calves**. **Calves** means:
a. the back part of the lower leg
b. a quick view

Name _____ **Date** _____

Spelling: /aw/ and /ow/

Focus The /aw/ sound sounds like the word *dawn*. Two ways it can be spelled are:

aw   p<u>aw</u>   *au*   h<u>au</u>l

The /ow/ sound sounds like the word *cow*. Two ways it can be spelled are:

ow   pr<u>ow</u>l   *ou*   pr<u>ou</u>d

Practice | shawl   tower   pause   pounding   clown   tawny |

Consonant-Substitution Strategy
Replace the underlined letter or letters to make a spelling word from the box. Write the word on the line.

1. <u>cl</u>ause + p = _____   **4.** <u>cr</u>awl   + sh = _____

2. <u>t</u>own   + cl = _____   **5.** <u>p</u>ower   + t   = _____

3. <u>br</u>awny + t = _____   **6.** <u>s</u>ounding + p   = _____

Spelling • *Reteach*

UNIT 6

Possessive Nouns and Pronouns

Name _____ Date _____

Focus

- **Possessive nouns** show ownership. They end with apostrophe s ('s), or s apostrophe (s') for plural nouns that end in s.

- **Pronouns** take the place of nouns and must agree in number and gender.

  Pronouns: *I, you, he, she, it, they, we*

- **Possessive pronouns** can be used in place of possessive nouns.

  Possessive Pronouns: *my, your, his, her, its, their, our*

Practice **Rewrite each phrase using a possessive noun.**

1. The desk that belongs to Phillip _____

2. The house that belongs to my grandparents

_____

Rewrite each sentence using a possessive pronoun.

1. The teacher's car is blue. _____

2. Beth's shoe was untied. _____

Name _____ Date _____

Phonics: Unit 6 Review

Focus
- /ō/ and /ow/ spelled ow

  Example: /ō/ = blow   /ow/ = cow
- /o͞o/ and /ū/ spelled ew and u_e

  Example: /o͞o/ = blew, tune   /ū/ = few, cube
- /o͞o/ and /oo/ spelled oo

  Example: /o͞o/ = food   /oo/ = foot
- **Silent Letters** are letters in a word that are not heard when the word is read.

- **Consonant Blends** are when one or more consonants appear together in a word and each consonant keeps its sound.

Practice Identify the sounds for the spelling *ow* in the following words.

1. show _____   **2.** plow _____

Identify the sounds for the spelling *-ew* or *u_e* in the following words.

1. tube _____   **2.** flew _____

Underline the silent letter and circle the consonant blend.

1. answer   **2.** scream

Phonics • *Reteach*

Name _____ Date _____

Homographs and Homophones

 Focus

- **Homographs** are words that are **spelled and pronounced the same** but **differ in meaning.**

- **Homophones** are **words that sound the same** but **have different spellings and meanings.**

Practice Circle the correct meaning for the boldfaced word in each sentence.

1. Jerry forgot to wind his **watch.**
   a. a device that shows time   **b.** look at something carefully

2. Could you bring your **bat** to the game?
   a. a mammal that flies   **b.** something you use to hit a ball

would	choose	do	maid	break

Find a word from the box that is a homophone for each numbered word.

1. dew _____   **4.** wood _____

2. brake _____   **5.** made _____

3. chews _____

Name _____ Date _____

Selection Vocabulary

Focus   treated   union   border   crops
          strike   boycott   weakened   awarded

Practice   Circle the best definition for the word in bold.

1. The farmer worked hard to get all of his **crops** planted. Does **crops** mean:

   a. fruits, vegetables, and other plants
   b. a group of workers who join together for better pay and work conditions

2. Last year, I was awarded a certificate for perfect attendance. Does **awarded** mean:

   a. grow less strong
   b. given a prize

3. The workers will **strike** if they don't receive longer lunch breaks. Does **strike** mean:

   a. to stop work in order to get better pay and conditions
   b. a line where one country ends and another begins

4. People who saw the signs began to **boycott** the store to support the workers. Does **boycott** mean:

   a. to refuse to buy something until workers are treated better
   b. to behave toward in a certain way

Selection Vocabulary • *Reteach*

Name _____ Date _____

Drawing Conclusions

Focus **Readers** can use information from the writer to draw conclusions about the story.

- To **draw a conclusion,** a reader should use information that a writer gives about a thing, character, or event.
- Conclusions must be supported by information in the story.

Practice A **Draw a line under the conclusion that is best supported by the information.**

During the summer, many birds in the north build nests and have babies. Birds have a hard time finding food when the weather gets colder. Some birds fly south when they can't find food. Migrate means "to move from one place to another."

Conclusion A: Birds migrate south for the winter.

Conclusion B: Birds never migrate.

Alfonso couldn't finish his breakfast. He had prepared a speech about the history of his school. Alfonso's knees wobbled when he walked toward the gym. He had never given a speech in front of the whole school before.

Conclusion A: Alfonso did not go to gym class.

Conclusion B: Alfonso was nervous about giving a speech at school.

Copyright © SRA/McGraw-Hill. Permission is granted to reproduce this page for classroom use.

Name _____ **Date** _____

Drawing Conclusions

Some men and women are putting up a large tent. A sign next to the tent says "Circus." A train brought elephants, tigers, and other animals into the station. Acrobats are practicing tricks on a trampoline near the tent.

Conclusion A: The circus is in town.

Conclusion B: The circus is leaving.

Practice B **Draw a conclusion based on the sentences.**

- Gardening requires lots of tools.

- It is important to know which flowers and vegetables need a lot of sun.

- Weeds need to be pulled, and plants need to be watered daily.

- Sometimes insects can damage plants.

Conclusion: _____

Comprehension • *Reteach*

Name _____ Date _____

Spelling: Review

Practice | law allow boot low spring arrow book

Visualization Strategy

Read each pair of words below. Circle the correctly spelled word. Then write the word on the line.

1. spering   spring   _____

2. arrow   aroe   _____

3. lau   law   _____

4. boot   bute   _____

5. alau   allow   _____

6. loe   low   _____

7. book   buke   _____

Name _____ Date _____

Conjunctions and Compound Sentences

Focus

- **Conjunctions** connect words or groups of words in a sentence. The words *and, but,* and *or* are commonly used conjunctions.

- **Compound Sentences** are two sentences joined together by a conjunction.

- Reminder: put a comma before the conjunction when combining sentences.

Practice **Combine the following sentence pairs using conjunctions.**

I climbed up the slide. I slid down.

_____

It was past my bedtime. Mom let me stay up to see the

movie. _____

_____

We could build a snowman. We could go sledding.

_____

_____